THE INTERNATIONAL
WILDLIFE
ENCYCLOPEDIA

VOLUME 19

THE INTERNATIONAL
WILDLIFE ENCYCLOPEDIA

GENERAL EDITORS

Dr. Maurice Burton

Robert Burton

MARSHALL CAVENDISH CORPORATION / NEW YORK

CONTENTS

Vapourer moth

The most distinctive feature of the vapourer moths is the great difference between the males and females. The males are active little moths, with a wingspan of just over 1 in. They fly mainly in sunshine, although they are recorded as coming to an artificial light at night. Most of the females, and certainly all those of the European species, are wingless and look like fat six-legged spiders, and they are so inactive that they never leave the cocoons which enclose their pupae. The larvae feed usually on the leaves of various trees and bushes, but that of one European species lives on heather.

The name was first given to the species **Orgyia antiqua** in 1782. A vapourer then was the term for a braggart or a tongue-wagging talker. The male of the vapourer moth is reddish brown and almost the only decoration on its wings is a white eye-spot on the rear of the forewings; there is no white mark at the tip of the wings. There is nothing to boast of in this, so the name may have been suggested by the male moth's fluttering flight.

The vapourer is one of the tussock moths and its common name was later given to related species, such as the scarce vapourer and the heather vapourer. There are other related species in temperate Asia and a closely related North American species is the white-marked tussock moth.

△ *Confined for life: the common vapourer female lays her eggs on her cocoon. Her life history is simple — she develops and mates in her cocoon, lays her eggs on it and then dies.*

Wind-blown caterpillars

The common vapourer moths hatch from the pupae in late summer. The females remain in their cocoons where the males seek them out, guided by their scent. Even dead and preserved females have been known to attract males into a room with an open window. Having mated the female lays her eggs on the surface of the cocoon and then dies. The young larvae are covered with very long hairs and have the habit, in common with many small caterpillars, of letting themselves down on silken threads when alarmed. They are then easily blown about by the wind, like thistledown, and may travel long

2521

distances. This is, in fact, the only means of dispersal they have, apart from the larva's limited powers of crawling, since the female is completely sedentary.

Male and female caterpillars

The grown larvae are prettily coloured, and ornamented with tufts and strands of hair. If a cocoon covered with eggs is found and the larvae are hatched and reared in captivity a curious activity will be seen. About half of them reach maturity and pupate while the rest feed for about ten days longer and grow to a much larger size before spinning their cocoons. Then, on opening one of the earlier cocoons and one of the later their respective pupae will be seen to differ both in size and appearance.

The smaller ones are males and the larger ones females. This is one of the rare instances in which the sex of a caterpillar can be recognised. The males are the first to appear after pupation. The females, however, begin to emerge long before the last of the males, so the time lag is less marked than it was in the pupating stage.

A grisly cradle

The three European species show an interesting sequence in the degree to which the females become inactive. The female common vapourer comes right out of the cocoon and lays her eggs on its outside. The female scarce vapourer lays them between the inner and outer layers of the cocoon, while the female heather vapourer stays right inside the cocoon for mating and dies there as well, her eggs overwintering in her dead, dried-up body. In a South African species *Bracharoa dregei*, closely related to the vapourer moths, the female behaves rather like that of the heather vapourer, but her eggs hatch soon after mating and the larvae make their first meal of their mother's still-living body.

The North American white-marked tussock moth is similar to the European vapourer in appearance and habits. It is sometimes a minor pest of trees and shrubs. In a Japanese vapourer the male is a normal vapourer moth but there are two forms of the female, one fully winged and resembling the male but larger, and one with vestigial wings.

Why no wings?

There are a number of species of moths with wingless females, but in almost all cases they are species in which mature moths emerge in winter. The winter moth, a notorious pest of orchards, is an example. It has been suggested that if the females of such species had wings, winter gales might blow them far away from the place where they lived as larvae, perhaps even out to sea, where they would perish.

No such explanation can be given for the vapourer females, and the reason for their wingless condition remains a mystery. All that can be said is that there is a tendency for the females of all tussock moths to show a reluctance to fly. The female gypsy moth, for example, never flies although she is fully winged, and the larvae of gypsy moths are known to be dispersed by wind like those of the vapourers. It is of interest that the Japanese vapourer has both winged and wingless females.

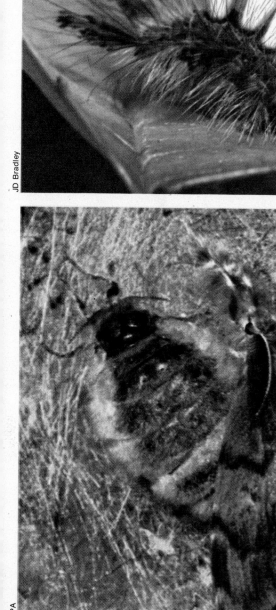

JD Bradley

G Temple: NHPA

class	**Insecta**
order	**Lepidoptera**
family	**Lymantriidae**
genera & species	*Orgyia antiqua* common vapourer **O. ericae** heather vapourer **O. leucostigma** white-marked tussock **O. thyellina** Japanese vapourer **O. recens** scarce vapourer others

△ *Bizarre but beautiful: the caterpillar of the common vapourer moth displays its ornamental tufts and strands of hair. When handling this larva care must be taken as the hairs can cause severe skin irritation.*
◁ *The sluggish female and winged male common vapourer moths on their cocoon. The male's only attributes are the white eye-spots on his wings. They occur practically over the whole of Europe, and also in northeast Asia Minor, Armenia, Siberia and North America.*

Velvet ant

Velvet ants are some of the biggest frauds in the animal kingdom. Although called ants they are, in fact, solitary wasps. Their common name is due to the marked difference between the male and female. The female is wingless and is therefore forced to run about over the ground, looking like a big hairy ant. The male is winged and so attracts little attention among other wasps that fly around.

The bodies of velvet ants are covered with a pile of short velvet-like bristles, often patterned in black, bright orange and scarlet. Even the antennae are covered with these short hairs. The 3 000 species are all much alike in colour, and most of them live in the hotter, drier parts of the world, and especially in America. A few live in temperate latitudes, including Europe, and two live in Britain. All velvet ants are parasitic on the larvae and pupae of other insects, including bees and wasps. There are even velvet ants that parasitize other solitary wasps, the hunting wasps, that themselves prey on other insects. Some of the desert species have a thick covering of long whitish hairs. The smallest velvet ant

Mutilla lilliputiana is $\frac{1}{8}$ in. long and the largest, **Dasymutilla occidentalis**, of the southeastern United States, is 1 in. or more long and is known as the cow-killer or mule-killer. The so-called large velvet ant of Britain **Mutilla europaea** is only about $\frac{1}{2}$ in. long. In many species the male is nearly twice the size of the female, but in the three for which sizes are given here the females are only slightly smaller than the males.

▽ *Wasp parasitizes wasp: a South African velvet ant lanys her eggs in the nest of a mud-dauber wasp; on hatching the larvae will eat the host's eggs. (Approx × 15.)*

Well armed and defended

Velvet ants are equipped for entering the nests of bees and other wasps; they are not only armed but armoured. They have unusually thick and hard outer coverings and entomologists report having difficulty in pushing a steel pin through the thorax of a dead velvet ant when adding a specimen to their cabinet. The males are without a sting and can be handled with impunity. The female, however, has a long and formidable sting, although the power of its venom has often been exaggerated. There is no reason to suppose, for example, that it could cause the death of a large quadruped such as a mule or cow. The female can, however, sting the hand painfully, if handled carelessly, and it is presumably lethal to the insects, such as bumble-bees, whose nests the velvet ants parasitize.

Both male and female of the large velvet ant make a squeaking sound by stridulation, using a file-and-scraper type of organ which is situated about halfway along the upper surface of the body.

The female velvet ants are usually encountered running actively on the ground near the nests of the species which they victimise, or they may be found actually in the nests if these are opened up. The males visit flowers and are generally noticed only by entomologists with specialised knowledge.

A rough wedding

In temperate regions males and females appear and mate in spring. Professor HM Lefroy, in describing the mating of tropical species, spoke of the males as powerful insects. When one finds a female he 'seizes the female by the thorax and flies off; on some convenient spot he mates with her, clasping her firmly to him by his forelegs and standing erect on the others . . . in the frequent intervals the male shook the female with a twisting motion as we would shake a bottle whose contents we desired to mix.'

Eaten out of house and home

After mating, the female runs about, probably covering considerable distances, until she finds an established bumble-bees' nest, or the nest of whichever kind of insect she battens upon. Then she enters. She is well equipped to resist any attempts to evict her, and remains in the nest, feeding on the bees' store of honey, and eventually she lays her eggs in the pupal cells or cocoons of the bees, one egg in each cell. The larvae from these eggs feed on the host pupae, then they themselves pupate, coming out later as adult wasps. In temperate latitudes they pass the winter as pupae in the bees' nest, which is abandoned by the bees at the end of the summer.

There is a record of a bumble-bees' nest dug out of the ground containing 76 velvet ants and only two bumble-bees. This is probably an abnormally high number but it illustrates how effective the female velvet ant must be in coping with the efforts of the female bumble-bee, the rightful owner of the nest, to drive her out.

A coat to keep cool

The female 'velvet ant' wasp, by her appearance, tricked the ordinary person into giving her the misleading common name. The behaviour of both the females and the males made it difficult for scientists to study them. As a result not a great deal is known about them, and nobody seems to have carried out precise experiments to test why they should have such unusually hairy bodies. We can only guess that it serves as an insulating layer, the clue being that these insects are essentially desert and semi-desert dwellers. The camel's coat keeps in the heat during the cold nights in the desert and it also keeps out the heat of the sun by day. The female velvet ant, being wingless and forced to run over the hot sand by day, probably needs the insulating layer against the heat from the ground as well as from the sun. Her mate, in the case of most species of velvet ants, can keep cool by flying or perching in cooler air, but there are some species in which even the males have only degenerate knob-like wings, or are completely wingless.

AB Klots

Richard Cassell

phylum	**Arthropoda**
class	**Insecta**
order	**Hymenoptera**
family	**Mutillidae**

◁△ *Fur-coated in the desert: the hairs on the white desert velvet ant* **Dasymutilla gloriosa** *probably act as an insulating layer against the intense heat in the Arizona desert.*
◁ *A closer look shows that despite its ant-like attitude, its mouthparts are more typical of wasps.*

Venus' flower basket

The Venus' flower basket is the only deep-sea sponge at all well known outside scientific circles. In the second half of the 19th century its white, lacelike skeleton was treasured and given the place of honour in the best room in the house. It was also known as **regadéra,** the Spanish watering pot.

The 2 000 or more species of sponges live in marine and fresh waters, from between tidemarks to the depths of the oceans. The class to which the Venus' flower basket belongs is known as the Hexactinellida because they have a skeleton of six-rayed, or hexactin, spicules of silica. The Hexactinellida include most of the showy and beautifully delicate sponges as well as some of the largest and toughest. The Venus' flower basket skeleton is a 10in. curved tube, narrower at the base, where there is a tuft of hairlike spicules, and wider at the other end, which is closed by a perforated plate. This skeleton is covered by a thin layer of delicate flesh.

The Venus' flower basket lives in a relatively small area off the Philippines at depths of 600 ft. There are, however, related species in deep waters off Japan and in other parts of the western Pacific and the Indian Oceans.

▷ *Like fine white porcelain — the beautiful lattice-like skeleton of a Venus's flower basket. The skeleton of this six-rayed sponge retains the general body structure and symmetry of the living animal. A convex perforated sieve-plate strengthens the upper end.*

P Morris

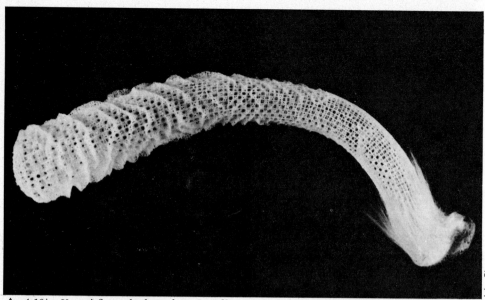

△ *A 10in. Venus' flower basket — the tuft of fibres at the lower end roots the living sponge.*

John Clegg

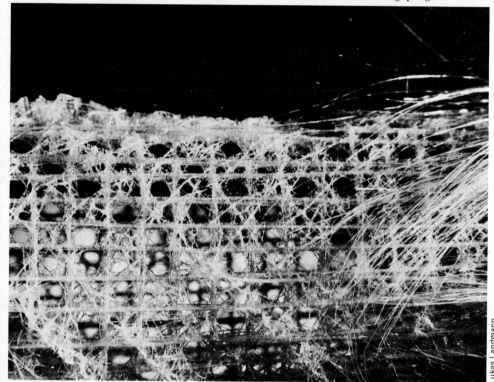

△ *Magnified: four of the six rays per spicule form this meshwork; the other two are tiny.*

Lukas Landmann

How does it live?

The largest of the six-rayed spicules have four very long rays and two very short, the longs rays being interwoven to form a remarkable strut and girder work, revealed when the sponge is cleaned of its flimsy flesh. This was once described by a professor of engineering as 'the finest example of civil engineering ever seen, combining maximum strength with minimum material'. The tuft of long slender spicules at the base of a Venus' flower basket is like glass wool, but each strand ends in a minute anchorhead, visible only under a microscope. The whole tuft is probably embedded in soft mud. Water flows through holes in the wall of the tube into a central cavity and then out through the perforated plate. In other kinds of sponges (p 168) their flagellated chambers create a current which draws water into the body through one set of holes and drives it out again through another set. The flagellated chambers of hexactinellids

are relatively large and thimble-shaped. Water flows passively through them. This led Dr George Bidder to suggest that the Venus' flower basket was not vertical to the seabed but that the curvature near its base meant it lay parallel to the sea floor.

Commonplace breeding

We can only presume that deep-sea sponges feed like sponges in shallower waters are believed to do, on minute particles of dead animal flesh or on bacteria, perhaps on both. Until 50 years ago even less was known about the breeding of Venus' flower basket. Then T Okada made a study of the whole life history of a related species. As in other sponges there are no special reproductive organs but sperms and ova are produced, in the breeding season, from body cells which grow much larger than usual. Presumably the sperms are released into the outgoing current, find their way to another sponge, enter it and fertilise the ova. These

then divide repeatedly to form embryos which are released later as oval larvae that swim around for a while before settling on the bottom to grow into new sponges.

Enforced fidelity

The Japanese species studied by Okada has been linked with the species originally called the Venus' flower basket because the two are very alike. Both also have a pair of inch-long prawns inside them. These enter as larvae on the incoming water current, change into prawns, grow and then cannot get out. There may be up to three of these prawns inside a sponge but sometimes there is none. Most commonly there is a pair which, imprisoned for life, must remain together. So the sponge containing them has been accepted as a symbol of conjugal fidelity. In 1901, Professor Isao Ijima wrote that the sponges are in demand 'on account of an old custom connected with the marriage ceremony'. This was to include one of them in the decorations in the room where the marriage ceremony took place. 'It is held to be a felicitous object betokening eternal connubial love on account of the presence of the inmates in an inseparable pair. In the long list of gifts which the present Emperor and the Empress of Japan received from their subjects on the occasion of their twenty-fifth wedding anniversary are mentioned several *Euplectella*, gifts humble in themselves but full of well-wishing sentiments.'

Wiped out for money

The sponge first called the Venus' flower basket, and the one brought in numbers to Europe, came from a small area 'about a quarter of a mile' off Zebu, Philippines. Captain William Chimmo RN, writing in 1878, suggested it had been fished out of existence. If this were true only avarice could be blamed. The first specimens sold to Europeans fetched £10 a pair. This led to a minor 'gold rush'; the market was glutted and the sponge lost its high value.

A fabulous sponge

Another related deep-sea sponge, from the Indian Ocean, has an equally romantic name. It is called *Regadrella phoenix*, the first part of the name meaning a small Spanish watering pot, the second part alluding to the legend of the phoenix. This was a mythical bird said to appear every 500 years to build a nest and then set fire to it. The phoenix was consumed in the flames but from its ashes arose a new phoenix. When the sponge *Regadrella phoenix* dies several buds are formed at its base and each may grow into a new sponge. This species must also have a limited distribution because very few specimens have been dredged up.

phylum	**Parazoa**
class	**Nuda**
order	**Hexactinellida**
family	**Euplectellidae**
genus & species	***Euplectella aspergillum*** *Venus' flower basket* ***E. oweni***, *others*

Vesper bat

There are 980 species of bats in 17 families. Nearly one-third of the species are in one family, the Vespertilionidae. They are usually referred to by those studying bats as the vespertilionids but it is not surprising that people with no special knowledge of them have simplified this to vesper bats. Since most of the 980 species of bats are seen in the evening, this simplified name is hardly specific; yet it is a convenient name for the small, commonplace, insectivorous bats seen especially in temperate latitudes, but found all over the world except at the poles.

Vesper bats are mainly small. They range from $1\frac{1}{4}-4$ in. head and body length, with wingspans of about $5-15$ in. Most of them are various shades of brown, sometimes grey or black, and a few are yellow, orange or red. Some, like the spotted or pinto bat of the United States and Mexico, have white patches. Vesper bats typically lack nose leaves but have an earlet. The ears, as in the barbastelle and the long-eared bat, may be up to $1\frac{1}{2}$ in., half the length of head and body.

Leisler's bat **Nyctalus leisleri** *hunting.*

Photos by SC Bisserot

Sleeping quarters

Most vesper bats spend the daylight hours in caves or cavities in hollow trees, under loose bark, among foliage, or, more especially, in rock crevices, buildings, tunnels, mine shafts and natural caves. They usually hang by their hindfeet and prefer to sleep on a vertical face rather than hanging free by the toes. Some are solitary but most roost in small groups or in colonies. The sexes often roost separately, especially when the females are giving birth or have young. Roosting places are often traditional, with the same colony using a particular place year after year. Some species move from a summer feeding ground to winter quarters, which may be several miles away. The red and hoary bats make long migrations southwards at the end of summer, returning the following spring.

Highly manoeuvrable wings

A bat's skeleton is light. The arm, which carries the wing membrane, consists of a short upper arm and a long forearm with a single bone, the radius, and a compact wrist with several of the bones fused together. The finger bones are greatly elongated, especially the third and fourth, which support most of the wing membrane. The thumb is short and bears a claw, used in climbing or walking. The wing membrane runs from shoulder to wrist, over the fingers and backwards along the side of the body to the ankle. It is made up of a double layer of skin between which are such slender elastic strands and fine muscle fibres that the wing collapses and folds up easily when not in use. While on the wing, however, a bat has full control through the tendons, which are worked by the arm muscles, controlling all the joints; it is, in fact, the most manoeuvrable of all flying animals. Among vesper bats there are the long-eared bats that fly through foliage and hover to pick insects off leaves and, at the other extreme, the slender winged noctule that often hawks high-flying insects.

While the bat is flying its wing acts as a ventilator; the network of fine blood vessels allows the blood to be cooled so the bat does not become overheated from the exertion of flying. When the bat lands and folds its wings the flow of blood to the wings is cut down, so the heat is retained in the bat's body as the surface area is reduced.

Feeding on the wing

Nearly all vesper bats are insect-eaters. They have sharp teeth, the molars having a W-shaped pattern of cusps for chewing. One species, the fishing bat of California, eats fish and small crustaceans, and a few other species are suspected of catching fish. The desert bats of North America catch insects near the ground and also capture scorpions and lizards. Most vesper bats eat only insects, which they catch in flight. Small insects are chewed and swallowed straight away. Larger prey such as moths and beetles is usually pouched in the interfemoral membrane, between the tail and the hindlegs, where the bat, being able to bend its head back under its body, can chew it while in flight.

Members of the Vespertilionidae come out at varying times in the evening, from just before sundown to almost dark. Some are still seen on the wing just before dawn, but

the night is divided into alternating spells of hunting and resting to digest their food. Some species, like the noctule, have only two periods of hunting, of an hour each.

Delayed fertilisation

Most of our information about the breeding of vesper bats is from species in temperate regions, where the bats hibernate. There, mating usually takes place between August and October, the sperms being stored in the female, and it may also occur again in spring. All fertilisation is in spring and after a gestation of 40–70 days, or even 100, according to the species, the babies are born from late May to July. In the tropics fertilisation follows immediately after mating. The number of babies at a birth is usually one or two, but there may be four.

Accidents in the dark

Because they fly by night bats probably have few enemies. Hawks have occasionally been seen to take them, well before nightfall. Owls have taken others, after dark. Domestic cats have on occasion been seen leaping up to capture a bat venturing too near the ground, so presumably wildcats sometimes take them. Despite the efficient echo-location system by which they find their prey and locate obstacles in pitch dark, there are records of bats seen flying into walls breaking their necks. Such accidents may be more frequent than we suspect.

Rip van Winkle bats

As a result of banding hibernating whiskered bats in the caves in Holland we know that 40% die in the first six months of life and beyond this the average expectation of life is about $4\frac{1}{2}$ years, but some of the bats have lived to 20 years or more. This is a remarkably long time compared with other small mammals of similar size, such as shrews and mice, which live only a few years, about five years in the longest-lived. The bat's effective life is, however, very brief. A noctule, for example, spends about six months of the year hibernating. In the remaining six months it is on the wing for about two hours in every 24.

◁△ *Reconnaissance: a noctule bat* **Nyctalus noctula** *looks, listens and sniffs before takeoff. The sharp teeth crush beetles, a favourite item in the noctule's diet.*
△ *European longeared bat, showing the skin 'bag' between the legs, which acts as both net and aerial larder in which to pouch large or hard insects on the wing.*

class	**Mammalia**
order	**Chiroptera**
family	**Vespertilionidae**
genera & species	**Antrozous pallidus** desert bat **Barbastella barbastellus** barbastelle **Lasiurus borealis** red bat **L. cinereus** hoary bat **Myotis mystacinus** whiskered bat **Nyctalus noctula** noctule **Pizonyx vivesi** fishing bat **Plecotus auritus** longeared (European) **P. macrotis** longeared (American), others

Vine pest

When Columbus discovered America he started a chain of events that nearly ruined the vineyards of France. Native to North America, the vine pest is a tiny insect related to the well-known aphides, also known as plant lice, greenfly and blackfly. The vine pest is called the vine phylloxera, sometimes referred to as the graperoot louse, although it also feeds on a wide range of other plants.

Except that the vine pest threatened to wipe out the vine-growing industry in France and elsewhere towards the end of the last century, there is little that is remarkable about it, other than its complicated life history. The vine pest was introduced into Europe between 1858 and 1863, when vine growers were experimenting with species of vines imported from America. By 1885 it had reached Algeria, Australia and South Africa. It also reached California about the same time, probably taken there on vines from other parts of the United States east of the Rocky Mountains that had been imported from Europe.

▽ *Ugly galls on the lower surface of a dried vine leaf, destructive work of the vine pest.*
▽▷ *The culprits, wingless and winged females.*
▽▽ *Healthy looking grape vines in Yugoslavia.*

Nearly vineyards' doomsday

From time immemorial only one species of vine has ever been used for wine-making in Europe. This is *Vitis vinifera*, a native of the region bordering the Caspian Sea, and it has proved extremely susceptible to attacks of the introduced vine pest. The presence of the aphid on a vine is shown first by the stunting of the plant itself and then in the reduction in the size and number of the leaves. In some cases the leaves become discoloured and galls form on their lower surfaces. At the same time knot-like swellings are found on the smaller roots. These turn from yellow to black and cause the roots to die and decay. The growth of the grapes is arrested and the fruits become wrinkled. When at its worst this pest ruined 2½ million acres of vineyards in France.

A complicated life history

After mating the female vine pest aphid lays her egg on the bark of the vine. Each egg passes the winter on the bark and in spring hatches, producing a wingless female called a fundatrix, or foundress. This female crawls into a leaf bud where she causes a gall to develop on the young leaf. Inside the gall she lays a number of eggs which develop into further wingless females called gallicolae, or gall-dwellers. These multiply during the summer, giving further gall-forming generations that in turn infest other leaves. Later in the season they produce another kind of wingless female, the radicicolae, or root-dwellers, which go down to the roots. After producing several generations of their own kind these radicicolae give rise to winged females which, in late summer, fly to other vines where they lay two kinds of eggs: small ones which produce males and large ones which produce females, both sexes being again wingless. The mouth-parts and digestive systems of this latest batch are not developed so they do not feed, but they mate and each female lays a single egg. These are the eggs which overwinter and which form the start of a new generation of fundatrix females which start the whole complex series again.

This is the typical, complete life history of a vine pest on its natural and native American host plants. When transferred to European vines the radicicolae are the principal form and they seem to be able to hibernate through the winter and reproduce their own kind indefinitely.

How it is controlled

The French vineyards are, happily, still productive. They were saved by intensive entomological research. There are many species of vine native to North America and these have varying degrees of resistance to the vine phylloxera. If European vines are grafted onto stocks of these resistant American plants the radicicolae are unable to thrive on their roots and the *Vitis vinifera* scions escape the effects of the pest. *V. riparia*, *V. rupestris* and *V. berlandieri* are American species of vine that are suitable for grafting, and hybrids between them and *V. vinifera* are also extensively used.

In the American grape-growing industry *V. vinifera* is cultivated on resistant stocks, as in Europe, and some resistant species of vines, producing fruit of different kinds and flavours, are also grown, including *V. labrusca* and *V. rotundifolia*.

Dangers of easy living

Aphides in general, and the vine pest in particular, have specialized mainly in the simple life. As insects go they are simple in structure, having few specializations other than the general features of the Hemiptera, the order to which they belong. Their food is simple and so is their method of feeding: they simply push their proboscis into the skin of a plant and suck. So, apart from enemies, life would be idyllic. By contrast, their methods of reproduction are highly complicated. Some pests have even more complicated life histories. The oak phylloxera, *Phylloxera quercus*, has no fewer than 21 different forms in its life history.

Complicated life histories, coupled with a high rate of multiplication, tend to be the rule for parasites. This can mean only one thing: that a complex reproductive cycle is needed for the species to survive. It is an indication that parasitism may bring an easy living but it is a precarious way of life.

Chris Howell-Jones

phylum	**Arthropoda**
class	**Insecta**
order	**Hemiptera**
family	**Phylloxeridae**
genus & species	***Phylloxera vitifoliae*** *vine pest*

Viperfish

The deepsea viperfishes are a fearsome sight because of their long fanglike teeth, which are slightly barbed at their tips. The teeth project on either side of the jaws.

The body of a viperfish ranges from 6–10 in. long, but its slender build makes it appear longer and it is only slightly thicker behind the head than in the tail. The head is small but has a strong lower jaw. The fins, including the tailfin, are also small, the pectorals being smaller than the pelvics. There is a small adipose fin, just in front of the tailfin, and opposite this on the underside are two small anal fins set close together. The most prominent fin is the first dorsal, set just behind the level of the rear end of the pectoral fins and it has a long whiplike spine formed from the first ray of the fin. The spine is about half the length of the fish and carries a small light organ at its tip. A double row of light organs runs all along either side of the lower body edge.

They live from 1 500–9 000 ft in oceans between latitudes 60° N and 40° S.

Viper or pike of the deep seas?

Usually, deepsea animals can be studied only from their dead bodies brought to the surface in nets. We are a little better off with viperfishes because we have the brief sightings by William Beebe who made the first descent into the ocean and saw one through the window of his bathysphere in 1934. In his book *Half Mile Down* he spoke of seeing a fine red prawn that was pounced upon by a 'really fearsome' viperfish which shook it for a moment then swallowed it. He also spoke of the viperfish's stomach that can stretch enormously as if it were made of rubber. The long body of a viperfish, with the second dorsal and the anal fins set far back, recalls the pike in fresh waters, which lunges swiftly at its prey, seizing it in a wide mouth armed with fearsome teeth. On the other hand a viperfish also has a lure—the light organ at the end of its whiplike dorsal spine—presumably used for tempting prey within reach. It also has 350 tiny light organs in the roof of its mouth and on the lower surface of the eyeball. Presumably these attract crustaceans and small fish near enough so when it opens its mouth to take in water for breathing they are drawn in. Thus a viperfish feeds as it breathes—at least so far as small prey is concerned.

Opening its throat

In the early 1950's Dr VV Tchernavin completed his brilliant anatomical studies of the viperfishes. He showed that the first vertebra behind the head is large and has broad surfaces for the attachment of strong muscles. The backbone, immediately behind this, is supple. The heart is well forward and lies between the bones of the lower jaw, as do the gills. In swallowing prey the muscles attached to the first vertebra pull the head up and, with the mouth opening at the same time, the lower jaw is shot forward, so the head seems almost to part company with the body as the throat opens at the sides. The effect is to give a wide and clear passage into the gullet. At the same time the heart is carried forward and the delicate gills outward, so they are not damaged by prey, even large prey, entering the throat. When the prey has been swallowed the head, jaws, heart and gills all return to their normal position. It is reasonable to suppose that with so much derangement of the vital organs, the swallowing action must be rapid. Digestion also seems to be very quick since most of these fishes have empty stomachs when caught.

Competition in depth

There are 300 million cubic miles of water in the oceans, room enough for the deepsea animals to be well spaced out. The study of many viperfishes suggests that in spite of all this space the various species are in competition with each other. There are three species of viperfishes. They are *Chauliodus danae*, *C. barbatus* and *C. sloani*, and the last of these is divided into 5 subspecies, two of which are *C. sloani sloani* and *C. sloani schmidti*. These two and *C. danae* live in the Atlantic, but each has its definite range which can be marked out on a map. In places their ranges are contiguous or even overlapping and where this happens it affects their vertical distribution. For example, in areas where *C. sloani sloani* is on its own it lives between 1 500 and 9 000 ft during the day—all viperfishes migrate into the surface layers at night. Where this is in the same area as *C. danae* it occupies only the depth from 3 000 to 5 400 ft, and *C. danae* occupies the rest.

class	**Pisces**
order	**Salmoniformes**
family	**Chauliodontidae**

◁ *A weird appearance is given by viperfishes because of their long fanglike teeth. This appearance has often led to them being used as illustrations of deepsea fishes although there are only three species of viperfishes and they certainly do not represent all the varied and numerous deepsea animal forms. The photophores or light organs can be clearly seen running along the side of the body as a double row and nearly extend to the tail. The three species of viperfishes occur in all oceans between latitudes 60° N and 40° S from tropical to very cold water and between 1 500 and 9 000 ft. Species: **Chauliodus sloani***

Vireo

Vireos are small, drably plumaged song-birds of the New World. The 42 species, together with the little-known shrike-vireos and peppershrikes, make up the family Vireonidae. In the 19th century they were known as greenlets but this name is now used for only tropical vireos of the genus **Hylophilus**. *Vireos range from 4 to 7 in. long and are usually olive-green or grey above and whitish or yellowish*

underneath. The bill is slender and sometimes bears a hook.

The best known is the red-eyed vireo, 6 in. long, olive-green above and whitish underneath. The top of the head is slate-grey and there is a white line with a black border running over the red eye. It breeds from central Canada to the shores of the Gulf of Mexico but is missing from most of the western half of the United States. One of the brightest vireos is the yellow-throated vireo of the eastern United States. It is olive-green above with two

white wing bars, a yellow eye-stripe and yellow on the chin, throat and breast. The greenlets are among the smallest vireos. The grey-headed greenlet is 4 in. long with a grey head and a white ring around the eye. The body is olive-green above and white and yellow underneath.

The vireos range from central Canada to northern Argentina, including the West Indies and the Bahamas and the slender-billed vireo is confined to the tiny island of Fernando de Noronha, 250 miles off the Brazilian coastline.

◁◁ *Devoted to incubation, this red-eyed vireo will not easily be persuaded to leave its nest — vireos have very strong parental urges. The nest is a deep cup of grass and strips of bark in which 3 or 4 spotted eggs are laid.*
◁ *The white-eyed vireo* **Vireo griseus** *has drab plumage typical of most of the family.*
◁▽ *An adult red-eyed vireo tries to satisfy the insatiable. The nestlings are fed mainly on insects and the parents share the task of food-collecting, although usually, as here, it is the female who works the harder.*

zontal fork by cobwebs. The female does most of the building and lays a clutch of 3 or 4 eggs in temperate regions or 2 or 3 eggs in the tropics. They are white or cream with brown or lilac spots. Incubation lasts 12–14 days and the male helps, although he sits for a shorter time than the female. The males are such dedicated singers that they even sing while sitting on the nest. Not all males incubate, however, and in those species in which males do not share incubation they do not brood the young either. Otherwise, the urge to incubate is very strong and vireos sometimes have to be lifted off the nest in order to count their eggs. They may even peck at the offending hand. The chicks are fed by both parents, the female bringing most of the food, and they start to fly when about 2 weeks old.

Trans-Atlantic immigrants

Although their distribution is American, red-eyed vireos occasionally turn up in the British Isles, especially on the western coast of Ireland and on the Scilly Isles, off the southwestern tip of England. The red-eyed vireo is one of a growing band of American birds that have been seen in the British Isles. These new migrants include the pectoral sandpiper *Erolia melanotos,* various ducks and cuckoos, the American robin, the bobolink *Dolichonyx oryzivorus* and the Baltimore oriole *Icterus galbula.* Shore birds and water birds might be expected to make the crossing but many trans-Atlantic migrants are small passerines. Some may have escaped from local aviaries but others definitely have not. It has been suggested that, having been blown out to sea, these small birds hitch lifts on ships for the rest of the way. However, they could not survive so long without food, many being insect-eaters, and if hitch-hiking were the answer, there should be as many records of European birds reaching North America. In fact, there seems to be a very good reason for thinking that the vireos and others are swept high across the Atlantic by the jet-streams in a few hours. Probably whole flocks are caught up but few birds make a landfall.

Monotonous songs
Except for some, like the red-eyed vireo, which lives in trees, most vireos live in undergrowth or thickets. They are not easy to see as they flit through the foliage, their drab colours making them 'just another small brown bird' to all but bird watchers, who often find it easier to identify them by their voice or habits.

A few vireos have pleasant songs, such as that of the warbling vireo of North America and the brown-capped vireo of tropical America. The songs of these two birds are continuous warblings. The other vireos are also persistent songsters but there is little that is musical about them. The red-eyed vireo was once known as 'the preacher' from its boring, rambling utterances. Each phrase consists of a variety of half a dozen notes, and one indefatigable ornithologist counted 22 917 phrases from one red-eyed vireo in one day. This was an average of over 1 000 an hour. The white-eyed vireo varies its collection of clicks and mews with mimicked notes of other birds.

Many of the North American vireos are migratory, spending the winter in Central America. The red-eyed vireo migrates across the Gulf of Mexico, down Central America and into South America as far as southern Brazil.

Foliage searchers
Vireos feed mainly on insects, their larvae, spiders and a few small fruits. The insects and spiders are sought among the foliage which the vireos move through with agility, sometimes hanging upside down to search the undersides of leaves. Large insects are held down with one foot and attacked by thrusting and tearing with the bill. Only rarely do vireos search for food on the ground. Red-eyed vireos sometimes descend to feed on small snails.

Singing on the nest
The nest is built in a tree or bush, sometimes near the ground but never on it. It is a deep cup of grass, leaves, strips of bark and other materials and is slung in a hori-

class	**Aves**
order	**Passeriformes**
family	**Vireonidae**
genera & species	*Hylophilus decurtatus* grey-headed greenlet *Vireo gilvus* warbling vireo *V. flavifrons* yellow-throated vireo *V. gracilirostris* slender-billed vireo *V. olivaceus* red-eyed vireo others

Viscacha

The plains viscacha and mountain viscacha are South American rodents closely related to the chinchilla (p 432). They are different in both form and habitat. The plains viscacha is heavily-built; an adult male may weigh as much as 15 lb. The body is up to 2 ft long with a short 6—8in. tail. The head is large and blunt with prominent black whiskers. The tail, which is fully furred, is short and stiff and helps the animal to sit upright. The four fingers on the forefeet are well-developed for burrowing and the three toes on the hindfeet have very sharp claws. The fur is coarse and fairly long, dark grey above with white underparts and black and white stripes on the face. The female is smaller with somewhat lighter fur.

The mountain viscacha, sometimes called the mountain chinchilla, looks more like a chinchilla or a long-tailed rabbit. It is smaller than its plains relative, $12\frac{1}{2}$—$15\frac{3}{4}$ in. long in head and body with a long tail, up to $12\frac{1}{2}$ in. It is a much slighter animal, weighing up to only $3\frac{1}{2}$ lb. It has large, erect ears and unlike the plains viscacha the claws on the fore- and hindfeet are blunt and weak. The fur is short, thick and soft. The upper parts vary from fawn to dark grey and the underparts are whitish, yellow or light grey. There is a crest of stiff hairs on the tail, which is black to reddish brown, and it often has a black stripe down the back.

Today there is only one species of plains viscacha, found over most of Argentina, and spreading into southern Brazil. Another species **Lagostomus crassus** is now almost certainly extinct. The four species of mountain viscacha are found in the Andes and its foothills, up to a height of 17 000 ft, from Peru and Bolivia southward to the Argentine.

Social animals

Both the plains and mountain viscacha live in colonies, the former on the pampas and scrubland and the latter in rugged, mountainous country wherever water and food are available. The plains viscacha digs extensive burrows, with long tunnels and numerous entrances, known as viscacheras. Some have been in continual use for centuries and sometimes cover as much as 200 sq ft. Colonies of 15—30 individuals are usually formed, ruled over by a single adult male. They are very clean rodents, carrying all their refuse up to pile on the excavated earth at the entrance to the burrow. The entire surrounding area is cleared and they seem to have a passion for collecting objects and adorning the earth mounds with them. Stones, bones, cow-dung, branches and even objects accidentally dropped by man are dragged to the burrows and placed on top of the mounds.

The plains viscacha is nocturnal, coming out to feed in the evening. It shares its

▷ The range of the mountain viscacha extends over mountainous country high in the Andes, and is quite separate from that of the pampas-dwelling plains viscacha.
△ △ The two kinds of viscacha differ in appearance as well as in habitat. A big head with short ears and a distinctive facial stripe are the most noticeable features of the portly plains viscacha, in contrast with its smaller mountain cousin (overleaf). Plains viscachas construct large mounds over their warrens, which were once scattered over the pampas in such numbers as to create a serious hazard to horsemen. Objects of all kinds are collected by the viscachas and displayed on the mounds.
△ Unlike the mountain viscacha, the plains viscacha produces only one litter a year, and the two offspring are slower to mature.
◁ Portrait of an inveterate collector.

Viscacha
■ Mountain
(Lagidium peruanum)
▨ Plains
(Lagostomus maximus)

△ *The chinchilla-like mountain viscacha is
less houseproud than the plains viscacha. It
does not excavate warrens, but lives in rock
crevices high in the mountains.*

burrows with many other creatures; owls,
snakes, lizards and even skunks. It is also
friendly with its own kind and occupants of
neighbouring colonies visit each other during the night. It has a variety of calls from
grunts and squeals to a wire-twanging sound.
The warning note is a peculiar swishing
noise followed by a liquid note which sounds
like a drop of water falling into a pool.

The mountain viscachas have a very
different way of life. Although living in
colonies of up to 80 individuals they do not
burrow but shelter in rock crevices or among
piles of boulders. Unlike their relatives on
the plains they are diurnal and spend most
of the day basking in the sun. They feed in
the evenings but always return to shelter
before dark. They are very agile, running
among the rocks and leaping up the moun-
tainside with their long hindlegs.

Devastation of grassland

The plains viscachas feed on a wide variety
of grasses, roots, stems and seeds. They are
voracious feeders, often laying bare large
areas of grassland. In captivity they will also
take carrot and potato. The mountain viscachas feed on plants—grasses, moss and
lichens found near their colonies.

Slow breeding

The plains viscacha is a slow breeder. After
a gestation of slightly less than 5 months,
two young are born in September. There is
only one litter a year and the young do not
reach maturity for 2 years. The mountain
viscacha mates in October and November
and usually only a single young is born after
a gestation of about 3 months, but there may
be 2 or 3 litters a year. The young are able
to nibble plants an hour after birth and males
become sexually mature in 7 months.

Plains viscacha on the blacklist

Now that the puma has disappeared from
its range the plains viscacha has virtually
no enemy except man. Owing to the wide
devastation of areas by the rodent's burrowing and its voracious appetite for grass it is
now regarded as a serious pest and in the
past few years it has been cleared from many
areas of Argentina, especially where grazing
animals are kept. It is not eaten by the local
people nor is its fur valuable but a few years
ago canned viscacha began to be exported
to Italy where it proved to be very popular.

The mountain viscacha on the other hand
is hunted by the local people for food and
for its hair which is mixed with wool and
made into a yarn. It also has a natural enemy
in the Andean fox. All species are now
sparsely distributed throughout their range
and the mountain viscacha, in particular,
seems in some danger of extinction.

Live trapping

Various methods of exterminating the plains
viscacha have been tried out, including
stopping up the entrances to starve the
animals out and flooding. In a fairly recent
expedition to obtain live animals for study,
because so little is known about them,
several methods of catching live viscachas
were tried out, including digging out and
vibration. The only methods that met with
any success were flooding and trapping.
Some were caught as they fled from their
viscachera after it had been flooded but
the majority were caught by trapping. All
the holes to the viscachera were stopped up
and wire-mesh treadle traps set at the most-
frequented holes. The traps were examined
at dawn and dusk and re-set in fresh holes
if no animals had been caught after two
visits. This method caught two or three
viscachas every day until a total of 151
animals had been captured.

class	**Mammalia**
order	**Rodentia**
family	**Chinchillidae**
genera & species	***Lagidium peruanum*** mountain viscacha **_Lagostomus maximus_** plains viscacha, others

Viviparous lizard

The viviparous or common lizard could be said to be a typical lizard. It has a slender body with a long tapering tail and well-developed limbs, a short, flat tongue, not deeply forked, external ear openings and the two halves of the lower jaw are firmly connected. The teeth are very small and conical, unfitted to deal with hard substances. It averages 5 in. in length, the female being slightly longer, with a maximum of about 7 in. The female is more heavily built, the male being the more graceful, his tail tapering gradually to a very fine tip. Although the tail is equal in length to the head and body in both sexes, that of the female appears shorter, owing to its sudden tapering beyond the thick basal portion.

It varies from yellow-grey to purple-brown above, with dark spots forming more or less broken longitudinal lines. There is sometimes a blackish line following the backbone to just behind the hips and a dark band edged with yellow along the sides. On the underside the males are orange or red, spotted with black. The females are orange, yellow or pale greenish, with or without black spots, or sometimes with only a few small grey dots. All-black, melanistic individuals occasionally occur.

The viviparous lizard lives farther north than any other European reptile. It ranges over most of Europe and Asia, except for southern and southeast Asia. It is found over the whole of the British Isles, including the Isle of Man, and is the only reptile found in Ireland.

Variety of habitat

The viviparous lizard, found in a wide variety of climates and habitats, is one of the hardiest reptiles. It lives as high as 8 000 ft in the Balkans and extends north of the Arctic Circle in Lapland. Elsewhere it is common on heaths, in open woods, in hedgerows, gardens and on sand dunes. It frequently basks in the sun and individuals have favourite spots such as a patch of sand or on an old wall. Sometimes as many as 50 have been seen lying together, basking, with their bodies flattened and limbs extended to catch as much sun as possible. Yet the viviparous lizard is intolerant of excessive heat. Indeed, in southern Europe it is found only in the mountain districts where it can keep cool.

The lizard is agile and graceful. Its movements are almost too quick for the eye to follow; and it is even more difficult to catch. It runs with a nimble glide, shooting forward in short dashes from one tuft of

△ Vantage point: a viviparous lizard seeks the warmest point on a rock. Although they enjoy basking in the sun, these reptiles cannot tolerate excessive heat.

herbage to the next, the body and tail scarcely lifted from the ground. It can also run easily over the tops of heather shoots, spreading its toes out to cover the gaps between the foliage. The claws are used to ascend vertical walls or even posts with smooth surfaces. The lizard can also swim well and will pursue prey in water. It has good hearing and is said to respond to some musical sounds. A few people have claimed they can attract it from its hiding place by a particular whistle. In the British Isles hibernation begins in October, the adults going before the young ones which, in a warm autumn, have been seen out in the south of England as late as November. It is one of the first reptiles to reappear in the spring. In the southern parts of its range this may be as early as February but usually it is in March, the males and young coming out first, the females some weeks later.

Fond of spiders

Viviparous lizards feed mainly on insects, including flies, beetles and moths, as well as ants and their larvae, and they are particularly fond of spiders. Small caterpillars are swallowed whole, large ones chewed, the insides swallowed and the skin rejected.

Living young

Mating takes place in April and May with no obvious courtship but with some fighting between the males. Gestation is about 3 months. As the name *vivipara* implies, the female retains her eggs until they are fully developed and ready to hatch. Thus the young are born free from the egg-membrane or else the membrane is broken either during or immediately after leaving her body. When kept in captivity the mother makes no attempt at a nest or concealment and seems to take no interest in her young. In the wild, however, she digs a shallow pit, preferably well concealed in moist soil, into which she deposits her young, in July or August. There are 5–8 in a litter, exceptionally 4 or 10. The baby lizards are 1½–2 in. long at birth. Most of them are bronze-brown but a few are born black and change to bronze-brown within a week. The underparts are greyish-brown and the back and sides are often speckled with gold. Within a few hours they begin to feed, hunting small soft-bodied insects such as aphides. From the first they are agile and skilful in the search for food. Males reach sexual maturity at 21 months.

Self-mutilation for safety

Large numbers of viviparous lizards fall victim to snakes, birds and other predators. Like many other species of lizards they are able to cast off the tail in order to elude an enemy and then grow a new one.

When attempting to catch a lizard, it is best to grasp it by the shoulders. If the tail is held instead, it will probably come away in the hand, snapping readily at a joint near the base. Another tail will grow from the stump if the lizard lives long enough, but it is always a poor, ungraceful affair compared with the original. General opinion is that the tail snaps off as a result of the mechanical pressure exerted in grasping it. In fact, the lizard actually throws off its tail. For example, it can happen that you grab the lizard by the body, yet the tail comes away, nevertheless. Conversely, tame lizards accustomed to being handled will not lose their tails even when held by them. The autotomy (self-cutting), as the operation is called, is governed by a nervous reflex and a special breaking point in the tail. At that point, there is a line of weakness through one of the vertebrae, almost cutting it in two. Opposite this point each blood vessel and nerve is narrowed as in the waist of an hour-glass. So everything is ready for the tail to be thrown off by muscular contraction with the least damage and shock to the animal itself. The narrow neck in each blood vessel at this point serves as a natural ligature and keeps bleeding to a minimum when the break comes.

When cast off, the tail continues to lash violently, so it twists and bounces in a truly startling manner. The predator's eye is held by this unusual spectacle, while the former owner glides like lightning into the nearest cover. It is easy to imagine how successfully the antics of the severed tail can divert attention from the escaping lizard.

J Blossom: NHPA

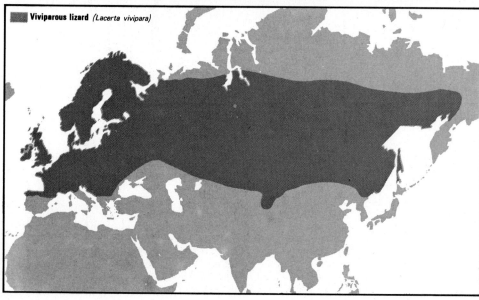

Viviparous lizard *(Lacerta vivipara)*

class	**Reptilia**
order	**Squamata**
suborder	**Sauria**
family	**Lacertidae**
genus & species	*Lacerta vivipara*

◁△ *The first steps of a live-born viviparous lizard watched by a solicitous parent. The egg-membranes of the other young have not yet ruptured, and the remains of the yolk may be seen inside them as well as the dark curved forms of the baby lizards.*

◁ *The viviparous lizard is quite widely distributed in northern and central Europe and temperate Asia. In the Alpine and northern Balkan countries it occurs mainly as a mountain dweller, ascending to 9 000 ft. It is the only reptile found in Ireland.*

Vulture

The name 'vulture' was originally applied to only the large, scavenging birds of prey of the Old World, but after the discovery of America the term was extended to the condors, turkey vultures and other members of the New World family of birds of prey. They resemble the Old World vultures in appearance, presumably through convergent evolution, both groups having similar habits.

Vultures have naked or nearly naked heads, and sometimes naked necks, which is an asset to birds that regularly thrust their heads into carcases. Unlike other birds of prey, which kill their food, they have relatively weak feet which are adapted for running rather than holding prey. Both groups of vultures have heavy bodies but they soar effortlessly for hours on their long, broad wings.

There are 15 species of Old World vultures, with dark brown or black plumage, except in a few cases. The bare skin of the head and neck may, however, be orange, pink or white. The European black vulture is the largest bird in the Old World. It has a wingspan of over 8 ft and weighs over 15 lb. The plumage is almost wholly dark brown or black, with pale skin on the head and neck. It ranges from Spain to Korea and Japan. At the other end of the scale there is the lammergeier, or bearded vulture (p 1274), and the Egyptian vulture. The latter has a wingspan of over 5 ft and is almost pure white except for black on the wings. The Egyptian vulture ranges through Africa, southern Europe, the Middle East and India. Only a little larger is the hooded vulture which is dark brown with a pinkish head and neck. It is very common in Africa south of the Sahara. The seven species of griffon and white-backed vultures are, perhaps, the 'typical' vultures. They are found throughout southern Europe, Africa and Asia, often in large groups, and they nest in colonies. They are medium-sized and have a ruff of long feathers around the naked neck. The remaining vultures are the palm-nut vulture, which has a feathered neck and black and white plumage, the white-headed vulture with blue at the base of the bill and the lappet-faced vulture. All of these live in Africa and have wattle-like folds of skin on the head and neck. There is also the Asian black vulture, which has a bright red head and neck.

▽ *White-backed vultures:* **Gyps africanus**.

Ripe food only

Vultures hunt by sight, detecting carrion from vast distances by watching the behaviour of other vultures and other carrion-eating animals. Large carcases may attract large flocks of vultures but despite their heavy bills most vultures have difficulty in breaking through the skins of large animals. Therefore they have to wait for the carcase to decompose or for another animal to attack it. The large vultures, such as the lappet-faced vulture, are powerful enough to rip through hide and, although solitary in habits, they take precedence over the gregarious griffon and white-backed vultures at a carcase. These, in turn, keep away the small vultures which have to be content with scraps.

The rasp-like tongues of vultures enable them to pull flesh into the mouth and their long necks allow them to probe deep into a large carcase, while the lack of feathers means that they have no problems about preening blood-stained feathers. Vultures do not feed on carrion exclusively, however. The largest vultures sometimes prey on the chicks of flamingos or on small rodents and the palm-nut vulture feeds on oil-palm nuts as well as shellfish from the seashore and sometimes hunts in shallow water for small fish.

Huge nests

Unlike the condors and many other birds of prey, the Old World vultures build their own nests instead of laying their eggs on the ground or in the abandoned nests of other birds. The lammergeier and the Egyptian vulture nest in caves or rock crevices, as do the griffon vultures which nest in colonies of over 100 on cliffs. The Indian griffon and the white-backed vultures often nest in trees, with up to a dozen nests in one large tree. The large vultures, the hooded vulture and the palm-nut vulture, nest singly in trees. The nests are huge cups of sticks and twigs lined with leaves, pieces of hide and refuse.

There is usually a single egg, two in smaller species, which is incubated by the female. Incubation ranges from 46 to 53 days, depending on the size of the vulture, and the chicks stay in the nest for up to $4\frac{1}{2}$ months. The male feeds the female while she is incubating, then both parents feed the chicks by regurgitation.

Decreasing scavengers

Vulture numbers are decreasing wherever modern agricultural methods and methods of hygiene are being introduced; there are fewer carcases left lying about, and those that remain have often been poisoned. Although the vultures are not so useful nowadays as scavengers around human settlements they still help to clear up the carcases of stock, which are a potential source of infection. Unfortunately they are not always seen in this light and are persecuted for allegedly killing livestock, although only the largest vultures could possibly attempt to do so.

◁ *Gregarious griffons. Cape vultures gorge on a common zebra carcase. Most vultures are not strong enough to rip the hide so have to wait for it to decompose.*

Okapia

2541

Riding the thermals

Vultures are most common in dry, open country where they can soar effortlessly in ascending air currents. They are also found in mountain country, up to 20 000 feet. Apart from supplying the air currents necessary for flight, these areas are also those where there is likely to be an abundance of carcases of large animals easily visible from the air. Vultures are rarely found in forests, except for the hooded vulture. This is the most widespread, although not the commonest vulture in Africa. It regularly scavenges around towns and villages, providing a valuable garbage disposal service, and even follows people as they till the soil, to feed on insects that are turned up. Because of its exploitation of man it is able to penetrate forests where there are human settlements.

To be able to soar at great heights, the heavy-bodied vultures make use of thermals, the 'bubbles' of hot air that rise from the ground as it heats up. A thermal is like a smoke-ring with a stream of air rising through the centre of the ring, which is spinning rapidly. The vultures glide around inside the ring, using the rising air to hold them aloft. This is the same principle as is used by glider pilots. The dependence of vultures on thermals is shown by their daily habits. They do not take off in the morning until the ground has warmed up and thermals begin to form. The lighter species of vulture take off before the heavier vultures, which need more lift.

▷ *With appetite obviously far in excess of stomach capacity, an Egyptian vulture attempts to break an outsize fake egg placed as part of a study into the stimuli initiating this species' extraordinary use of stones as tools. The stimulus was shape; a cube of the same size and colour as an ostrich egg was completely ignored. The vultures were very persistent; in this case a pair bombarded the fibreglass giant — its volume was equal to that of six ostrich eggs — for 1½ hours.*

▽ *Soaring in thermals. The thermal current begins as a rising column of warm air (1) undercut by cold air (2). Like a warm-air bubble (3 and 4) the thermal rises so strongly that a vulture circling in it will also rise.*

Tool-users

There are very few animals that use tools — the Galapagos woodpecker finch (p 616), the chimpanzee (p 429) and the sea otter (p 2076) are the best known — but in 1966 another was added to the list. This is the Egyptian vulture, which throws stones at eggs. The habit is so well developed in a population in Tanzania studied by Jane Goodall that it is surprising that there are no previous records. These vultures smash the tough shells of ostrich eggs either by throwing them against a rock or another egg, or by throwing a stone at them. If there is no stone nearby a vulture may search for one up to 50 yards away, fly back with it in its bill then sling it with a violent downward movement of the head. The action is repeated until the shell cracks. One vulture managed to throw a 2lb rock, and continued to do so for some time, no mean feat for a raven-sized bird.

class	**Aves**
order	**Falconiformes**
family	**Accipitridae**
genera & species	**Aegypius monachus** *European black vulture* **Gypohierax angolensis** *palm-nut vulture* **Gyps africanus** *white-backed vulture* **G. coprotheres** *Cape vulture* **G. indicus** *Indian griffon* **Necrosyrtes monachus** *hooded vulture* **Neophron percnopterus** *Egyptian vulture* **Sarcogyps calvus** *Indian black vulture* **Torgos tracheliotus** *lappet-faced vulture* **Trigonoceps occipitalis** *white-headed vulture, others*

Hugo van Lawick

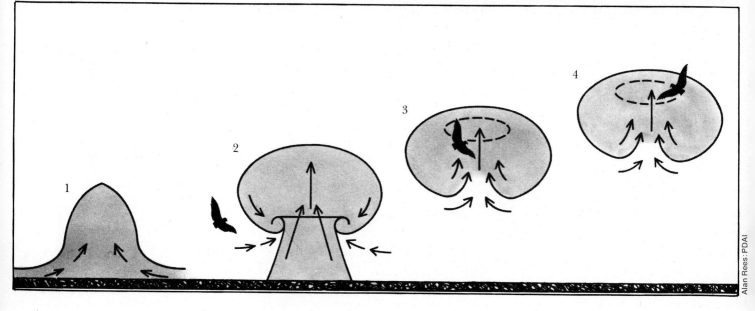

Alan Rees : PDAI

Wagtail

Wagtails are small birds closely related to pipits but with brighter plumage and characteristic long tails which continually 'wag' up and down. The bill is needlelike, typical of insect-eaters, and the feet are well developed with long toes. The tail is nearly as long as the head and body, making a total length of 6—7 in.

There are about eight species of wagtail, some of which are divided into races with separate common names. The race of the yellow wagtail that lives in Britain and on the nearest parts of the continent has more yellow in its plumage than the race which breeds farther east, and is known as the blue-headed wagtail. Both races are greenish brown above and yellow underneath with white outer tail feathers. The male of the British yellow wagtail has a bright yellow crown and eyestripe while the male of the continental race has a slate-blue crown, white eyestripe and white chin. The females are similar to each other but have the same eyestripes as the males of their race. The grey wagtail could easily be mistaken for a yellow wagtail as its underparts are yellow but it can be distinguished by blue-grey upperparts. The male has a black 'bib' in summer. Closely related to the grey wagtail is the mountain wagtail of Africa and the Madagascar wagtail. The pied wagtail also has two races which are easily confused. Both have distinctive black and white plumage but in summer the continental race, called the white wagtail, has a light grey back. The Cape wagtail of southern Africa is a close relative.

*Wagtails live in the Old World, but are not found in Australia. The yellow wagtail has, however, crossed the Bering Straits and breeds in western Alaska and the white wagtail has bred in Greenland. The forest wagtail is rather different from the others and lives in Manchuria and Korea. The willie wagtail **Rhipidura leucophrys** of Australia is one of the fantails (family Muscicapidae) which also has the habit of wagging the tail.*

Nod heads and wag tails

Wagtails usually live in open country, particularly in grasslands, but the pied wagtail is sometimes found in trees and often lives on farms and around houses. The forest wagtail of eastern Asia is found in woods. The pied and grey wagtails, particularly the . latter, are often found near water, sometimes wading into it. Many wagtails migrate, especially the yellow wagtail, the European population of which winters in Africa and occasionally reaches Australia from Asia. In winter many wagtails roost communally among dense vegetation

▷ *Pied wagtail—often seen dashing across a lawn on a seemingly pointless journey but really after a small insect seen with keen eyesight.*

or in trees. The pied wagtail may roost in the roof spaces of buildings, which may contain hundreds of birds.

The flight of wagtails consists of a series of 'bounds' as they alternately beat and close their wings. The glides between each burst of beating are longer than those in the flight of finches, and as a result the flight of wagtails is much more undulating. Their gait is also very characteristic. They run swiftly after insects on their strong legs with head, body and tail parallel to the ground, then stop suddenly and bob their tails rapidly. When walking normally the tail is bobbed and the head is nodded in time to the step.

Racing for food

Wagtails eat mainly small insects, particularly flies and insects living on the surface of the ground. Wagtails living near water feed on water insects such as small dragonflies and water beetles, small snails, and even minnows. The rapid, and seemingly pointless, dash of a pied wagtail across a lawn actually is the pursuit of a small insect which the wagtails' keen eyesight has detected. Most of the food is caught either on the ground or just above it, but wagtails can also be seen fluttering up to catch a higher-flying insect then dropping back to the ground. Yellow wagtails are found with cattle or sheep, feeding on the insects that they disturb.

Sitting on their tails

In his book *The Yellow Wagtail*, Stuart Smith has given vivid descriptions of the rivalry between male yellow wagtails at the beginning of the breeding season. Each male stakes out a territory and defends it against neighbours or other males which try to take it over. The owner advertises his possession by a warbling song and displays to rivals by throwing his head back, puffing out his breast feathers and leaning back on his

tail so it is flattened against the ground. Occasionally fights break out on the ground or in the air and rivals peck and claw each other.

Once territorial ownership has been settled and mating has taken place the female builds a nest, the male not assisting but merely escorting her. The nest of grass lined with hair is usually built among long grass or undergrowth. Pied and grey wagtails often nest in cavities in walls, banks or trees and sometimes use old birds' nests, such as those of blackbirds or dippers.

The clutch generally consists of 4–6 eggs, which are incubated for 2 weeks almost entirely by the female. The young are fed by both parents. They leave the nest after 2 weeks and continue to be fed, staying together as a family party for some time. The pied wagtail raises 2 or 3 broods a year, the male caring for one brood, while the female incubates the next clutch.

Why wagtail?

The Saxon name for the wagtail was *wagstyrt, styrt* meaning tail and its name in other languages also refers to the habit of bobbing the tail. In Dutch, the wagtail is *Kwikstaart* and in Danish *Vipstjert*. Tail-wagging is not confined to wagtails. It is well developed, but not so obvious, in the related pipits, and many other birds can sometimes be seen to bob their tails. The reason for tail-wagging remains obscure. It is probably related to their habit of suddenly dashing and fluttering after insects. The long tail acts as a counterpoise to the body and makes balancing easy as the wagtail stops dead or changes direction. Other birds can be seen to twitch their tails after landing. This movement, of which the wagtails' bobbing may be an extreme development, probably balances the bird, as we might wave our arms when unbalanced.

class	**Aves**
order	**Passeriformes**
family	**Motacillidae**
genera & species	*Dendronanthus indicus* forest wagtail *Motacilla alba alba* white wagtail *M. a. yarrellii* pied wagtail *M. cinerea* grey wagtail *M. clara* mountain wagtail *M. flava flava* blue-headed wagtail *M. f. flavissima* yellow wagtail *M. flaviventris* Madagascar wagtail others

▽ *Grey wagtail female with brood. It is easily mistaken for a yellow wagtail but can be distinguished by blue-grey upperparts.*

Wallaby

There are more than a score of wallabies. Some have been dealt with elsewhere: the pademelon (p 1671), quokka (p 1885) and the rock wallaby (p 1976). The way of life of the wallabies described here brings out other interesting aspects. In Australia itself the wallabies' story is largely one of persecution or extinction. There are also wallabies in New Guinea and one species of wallaby has become acclimatized to living wild in parts of Europe.

Most wallabies are the size of a hare or slightly larger, but the brush or scrub wallabies are up to 3 ft long in head and body, with a tail 2½ ft long and a weight of up to 50 lb. There are three species of hare wallaby, which are greyish brown with some red in places. The single species of banded hare wallaby is greyish with many dark bands across the back, from the nape to the base of the tail. The three species of nail-tailed wallabies are mainly grey but the eleven species of scrub wallaby are sandy to reddish brown. The five New Guinea forest wallabies are greyish brown to blackish brown.

Hares and organ grinders

Hare wallabies are so named not only for their size but for their habit of lying in a 'form', a shallow trench scratched in the ground, under a bush or grass clump. They also run fast and will double back on their tracks like hares. They are solitary, nocturnal and make a whistling call when pursued. Nail-tailed wallabies have similar habits except that when bounding along they hold their small forelegs out to the sides and swing them with a rotary movement, which has earned them the nickname 'organ grinders'. The purpose of the spur or nail at the tip of the tail is not clear. The scrub wallabies spend much of the day in cover but often come out to feed—although they never stray far from cover. They may be solitary or live in pairs, or in large groups. The New Guinea forest wallabies live in the rain forest from sea level to 10 000 ft, but apart from this there is little information on them, and it is assumed that they live much as other wallabies do.

Generalized diets

All wallabies are vegetarian, most of them eating grass, although the nail-tails eat mainly the roots of coarse grasses and the scrub wallabies take succulent roots and eat leaves as well. Probably, as with other herbivores, the diets as given here are oversimplified. Some wallabies, normally grass eaters, have been seen to eat bark and fruits, as well as leaves. There is also a lack of detail on the life history except that they probably carry one young in the pouch at a time.

Unfortunate wallabies

Piecing together such information as is available in Britain, it seems the wallabies dealt with here are among the 'unfortunates'. They are small enough to be at the mercy of introduced foxes and dogs; the

*Sunning itself: a swamp wallaby **Wallabia bicolor**. This position is adopted when the ground is cool.*

Harry & Claudy Frauca

fur of some of them is valued for export; their speed makes them targets for sport; and their flesh is agreeable as human food. The aborigines of Australia and New Guinea have hunted them for food, some species, such as hare wallabies, being persecuted more than others. The banded hare wallaby, now confined to a few islands in Sharks Bay, southwest Australia, was once numerous on the mainland. The aborigines used to burn the undergrowth to drive out the game, and this particular hare wallaby suffered badly as a result. The larger scrub wallabies have suffered from the general accusation that they are outgrazing the sheep (see p 2110) and cattle. The most recent research in Australia suggests this may have been exaggerated for all wallabies and kangaroos. Already it had been noted that the reverse was true for the banded hare wallaby—it was displaced by grazing sheep.

Some species of wallabies have become extinct, others are much reduced in numbers and range, and the only hope of ultimate survival for all seems to lie in creating suitable reserves and sanctuaries for them, and generally improving the climate of opinion in Australia.

Fate of immigrants

Australia is not the only part of the world where wallabies have had their ups and downs. Bernard Grzimek has summarised, in his *Four-legged Australians*, what has happened to Bennett's wallabies brought over to Europe. In 1887 Baron Philipp von Böselager released two males and three females in 250 acres of forest near Heimerzheim, in western Germany. In spite of one hard winter they multiplied to 35—40 in six years, but were later exterminated by poachers. At the beginning of this century Count Witzleben successfully bred Bennett's wallaby on his estate near Frankfurt-on-Oder—then shot them all because, he said, they frightened the deer. Prince Gerhard Blücher von Wahlstatt released wallabies on the island of Herm, Channel Islands, where they did well until British troops occupied the island and 'the entire herd found its way into their cookhouse'. Today feral wallabies live on the moors in Derbyshire.

One danger peculiar to temperate climates comes from ice on lakes, which tends to break, with fatal consequences, under the strain of a wallaby's heavy, rhythmical leaps.

Popperfoto

Pretty-face wallabies

△ *Relief! A contented wallaby closes its eyes as it sits down to scratch itself.*

▷ *Meal time. Incredibly this large young wallaby fits comfortably into mother's pouch.*

◁ *Heavyweight at home: the young wallaby causes an enormous bulge inside the pouch.*

class	**Mammalia**
order	**Marsupialia**
family	**Macropodidae**
genera & species	**Dorcopsis veterum** *New Guinea forest wallaby* **Lagorchestes leporoides** *hare wallaby* **Lagostrophus fasciatus** *banded hare wallaby* **Onychogalea frenata** *nail-tail* **Wallabia rufogrisea frutica** *Bennett's wallaby* *others*

G Thomson

Wall lizard

The wall lizard got its name originally from its habit of living in the walls separating fields. The adult male grows to a length of 8 in. including a tail of up to 5½ in. The female is slightly shorter. It has an elegant appearance, with a slender body and tail, a narrow, pointed head, and well-developed limbs with long, slender toes. The numerous small scales on the back are granular and there are six rows of larger scales on the abdomen. As in nearly all lizards, the tail is very brittle and readily shed, but can be regenerated. The wall lizard presents such an amazing variation in colour that it is almost impossible to give anything but the most general description. The ground colour varies from grey to red-brown or black, sometimes with a bronze or greenish tinge and with lines or a series of white, yellow or green spots along each flank. The lower flanks are spotted with blue, green or white. The underparts vary from a milky white to copper-red, often spotted with black. The male's throat is usually cream, bordered with reddish-brown or blue. In addition, the brightness and variety of their colours change as the sunlight flashes on them.

Up to 14 subspecies or local races of the wall lizard have been described, usually distinguished only by their colours. The wall lizard is found in central and southern Europe from Holland, Germany and Poland to the countries bordering on both sides of the Mediterranean as far east as Asia Minor. It is also found in the Channel Islands. Some 200 wall lizards were liberated in southwest England in 1937, where the climate is very similar to that of the Channel Islands. Although they were seen for some years they did not flourish and are now thought to be extinct.

Lively and agile

The wall lizard lives in dry regions among rocks, walls and old buildings and can sometimes be found in gardens, especially in rockeries. It is very lively and active, running so fast that it comes and goes in a flash. It is an expert climber, even up perpendicular walls. It sees and hears well and is very inquisitive, investigating anything out of the ordinary. Although it will swim if necessary it will drown if it does not reach the bank quickly. Like all lizards, the wall lizards love to bask in the sun but will retire to crannies or holes in the rocks in cloudy or rainy weather. Each has its favourite spot on a rock or wall where it may be found regularly. In southern Europe wall lizards can be seen in large numbers lying in the sun on almost every wall, rock or ruined building and at times they can become quite tame.

In the northern part of its range the wall lizard hibernates from October to March among stones or rocks or in holes in the ground. In the south the period of hibernation is much shorter.

Special sun spot? Both male (left) and female wall lizards have their own regular basking places.

Eric Hosking

Opportunist feeders

Wall lizards feed mainly on flies and other small insects or their larvae as well as on other small invertebrates. They will occasionally feed on fruit and soft plants. Like the European robin and other small birds, they will sometimes follow anyone working in the fields or garden to pick up the insects disturbed by the digging, and they have even been known to scramble about at the feet of picnickers, picking up any scraps of food.

Two or three clutches

In the wild the wall lizard mates usually in April, the female laying 3—9 oval white eggs in a hole dug in the soil. These hatch after about 2 months. There may be 2 or 3 clutches in one season. On hatching the young wall lizards are 1½—2 in. long. In captivity wall lizards live up to 3 years.

Attractive pet

With their beautiful colours and lively inquisitive ways wall lizards make charming pets. They are among the most popular of vivarium animals and every year thousands are exported from southern Europe. If kept in a vivarium it should be large and able to contain as many lizards as possible as wall lizards seem to like each other's company, running around seemingly playing with each other. The bottom of the vivarium should be covered in sand and there should be rocks and stones for the lizards to climb over and crevices where they can hide. There should also be some small plants and always a dish of water. They thrive on small earthworms, mealworms and other small soft insects and their larvae.

Colour preferences

Lizards will search for prey that eludes them and disappears from sight, making what look like purposive attempts to find it. They are helped by having keen eyesight and by an acute sense of hearing. A wall lizard living in a vivarium with a floor of dead leaves will search for a mealworm that crawls under the leaves, standing and turning its head from one side to the other, as if listening to the very slight, almost inaudible rustling. Then it will scrape over the leaves with its forefeet and pounce on the mealworm the moment it sees it.

Most lizards seem to show a preference for green, the commonest colour in their environment. Wall lizards living among rocks seem to be conditioned to preferring yellow, as well as orange and red, which may also be linked with their liking for fruit. They seem especially fond of the flesh of oranges, yellow plums and strawberries. When the lizard is in a vivarium, separated experimentally by glass from these fruits—the whole being so arranged that the lizard cannot receive the odour from them—it will make deliberate movements to reach the fruit, such as scratching the glass with its front feet.

class	**Reptilia**
order	**Squamata**
suborder	**Sauria**
family	**Lacertidae**
genus & species	*Lacerta muralis*

Walrus

Although hunted since the time of the Vikings, almost to the point of extinction, the walrus has survived and today, with strict conservation measures, some herds are very slowly recovering their numbers. The two subspecies, the Pacific walrus and the Atlantic walrus, differ in only minor details. The Pacific bulls average $11-11\frac{1}{2}$ ft long and weigh a little over 2 000 lb but they can reach $13\frac{3}{4}$ ft and weigh up to 3 700 lb when carrying maximum blubber. The Atlantic bulls average 10 ft long and up to 1 650 lb in weight but may reach 12 ft and weigh 2 800 lb. The cows of both subspecies are smaller, $8\frac{1}{2}-9\frac{1}{2}$ ft and 1 250 lb, but large Pacific cows may reach almost $12\frac{1}{2}$ ft and a weight of 1 750 lb.

The walrus is heavily built, adult bulls carrying sometimes 900 lb of blubber in winter. The head and muzzle are broad and the neck short, the muzzle being deeper in the Pacific walrus. The cheek teeth are few and of simple structure but the upper canines are elongated to form large ivory tusks, which may reach 3 ft in length and are even longer in the Pacific subspecies. The nostrils in the Pacific subspecies are placed higher on the head. The moustachial bristles are very conspicuous, especially at the corners of the mouth where they may reach a length of 4 or 5 in. The foreflippers are strong and oar-like, being about a quarter the length of the body. The hindflippers are about 6 in. shorter, very broad, but with little real power in them.

The walrus's skin is tough, wrinkled and covered with short hair, reddish-brown or pink in bulls and brown in the cows. The hair becomes scanty after middle age and old males may be almost hairless, with their hide thrown into deep folds.

The Pacific walrus lives mainly in the waters adjacent to Alaska and the Chukchi Sea in the USSR. The Alaskan herds migrate south in the autumn into the Bering Sea and Bristol Bay to escape the encroaching Arctic ice, moving northwards again in spring when it breaks up.

The Atlantic walrus is sparsely distributed from northern Arctic Canada eastward to western Greenland, with small isolated groups on the east Greenland coast, Spitzbergen, Franz Josef Land and the Barents and Kara Seas. They migrate southward for the winter.

Walruses also inhabit the Laptev Sea near Russia and do not migrate in the winter. It is thought that this herd may be a race midway between the Atlantic and Pacific subspecies.

▷ *A long-in-the-tooth bull walrus of the Pacific subspecies. The elongated upper canine teeth are put to a variety of uses, among them defence and digging for clams.*

Steve McGutcheon

JP Varin : Jacana

⊲ *Overleaf. Standing room only: the walrus is a sociable animal and crowded gatherings like this one used to be commonplace on some remote beaches. Persistent persecution by unscrupulous hunters has, however, reduced numbers and driven the walrus to new behaviour; the herds now tend to haul out onto the relatively inaccessible security of ice floes.*
⊲ *Playful pups: young walruses nuzzle each other with their sensitive moustaches.*

Slaughter by man

Walruses have been hunted by man from early times. The Eskimo and Chukchee have always depended on the annual kill to supply all their major needs, including meat, blubber, oil, clothing, boat coverings and sled harnesses. Even today they are largely dependent on it. The annual killings by the local people, however, had no very marked effect on the numbers of the herds. It was the coming of commercially-minded Europeans to the Arctic that started the real extermination. From the 15th century onwards they used the walrus's habit of hauling out on the beaches in massed herds to massacre large numbers in the space of a few hours. After 1861, when whales had become scarce, whalers from New England started harpooning walruses. Then they started using rifles and the Eskimos followed suit. More walruses could be killed but large numbers of carcases fell into the water and could not be recovered. An even greater wastage has been that caused by ivory hunters, who kill for the tusks and discard the rest of the carcase.

By the 1930's the world population of walruses had been reduced to less than 100 000 and only recently have strict conservation measures been enforced. The Pacific walrus now seems safe from extinction but the Atlantic walrus is still in danger.

class	**Mammalia**
order	**Pinnipedia**
family	**Odobenidae**
genus	***Odobenus rosmarus divergens*** *Pacific walrus* **O. r. rosmarus** *Atlantic walrus*

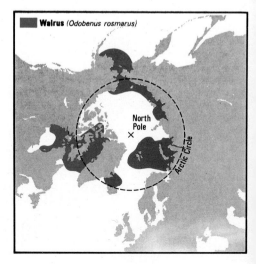

■ **Walrus** *(Odobenus rosmarus)*

North Pole

Arctic Circle

Tooth-walking bulls

Walruses associate in family herds of cows, calves and young bulls of up to 100 individuals. Except in the breeding season the adult bulls usually form separate herds. They live mainly in shallow coastal waters, sheltering on isolated rocky coasts and islands or congregating on ice floes. Since their persecution by man, however, walruses have learnt to avoid land as much as possible and to keep to the ice floes, sometimes far out to sea. They are normally timid but are readily aroused to belligerence in the face of danger. There seems to be intense devotion to the young, and the killing of a young one will rouse the mother to a fighting fury, quickly joined by the rest.

Walruses can move overland as fast as a man can run and because of their formidable tusks hunters, having roused a herd, have often been hard put to it to keep them at bay. Walruses have even been known to spear the sides of a boat with their tusks or to hook them over the gunwales.

As well as using them as weapons of offence and defence the walrus makes good use of its large tusks for digging food out of the mud and for keeping breathing holes open in the ice. It also uses them as grapnels for hauling itself out onto the ice, heaving up to bring the foreflippers onto the ice. The horny casing of bare hard skin on the palms of the flippers prevents the walrus from slipping. The walrus also uses its tusks for hauling itself along on the ice—indeed the family name Odobenidae means 'those that walk with their teeth'.

Walruses sunbathe and sleep packed close together on the ice floes with their tusks resting on each other's bodies. If the water is not too rough, adult walruses can also sleep vertically in the water by inflating the airsacs under their throats.

Clam grubbers

The walrus's diet consists principally of clams, which it grubs out of the mud with its tusks, and sea snails. It will also take mussels and cockles. The snout bristles help in detecting the shellfish. Clams are swallowed whole and no shells have ever been found in the stomach of a walrus, although it is not known how they are disposed of. A walrus also swallows a quantity of pebbles and stones, possibly for helping to crush the food in its stomach. Walruses usually dive for their food in shallow water of about 180 ft or less but occasionally they go down to 300 ft. It is not known how they deal with pressure problems at this depth but it may be in the same way as seals (p 502).

Occasionally a walrus, usually an adult bull, will turn carnivorous and feed on whale carcases or it may kill small ringed or bearded seals. Having sampled flesh it may continue to eat it in preference to shellfish.

Hitch-hiking pup

Most matings take place from late April to early June and after a gestation of just over a year one pup is born, every alternate year. Birth takes place on an ice floe. The new-born pup is 4 ft long with a coat of short silver grey hair and weighs 100—150 lb. It is able to swim immediately, although not very expertly, and follows its mother in the water. After a week or two it can swim and dive well. Even so, it usually rides on its mother's back for some time after birth, gripping with its flippers. After a month or two the silver grey hair is replaced by a sparser dark brown coat of stiff hairs. The cow nurses the pup for 18 months to two years but they remain together for several months after weaning. The pups grow quickly, males becoming sexually mature at about 5—6 years, the females at about 4—5 years.

Killed in the rush

Killer whales and polar bears attack walruses but not often, the polar bear particularly being wary of attacking an adult bull even when he is ashore and therefore more vulnerable. Panic when killer whales are near may, however, cause high mortality. In 1936 a large herd was attacked by killer whales and driven ashore on St Lawrence Island. They hauled out onto the beach in such panic that they piled up on each other and 200 of them are said to have been smothered or crushed to death.

Wapiti

The wapiti of North America is often referred to as cousin to the red deer (p 1924); the closeness of the relationship remains open to question. In the 17th century the wapiti—the name given by the Shawnee Indians—was an abundant and widely distributed deer in North America. Its range fell just short of the Pacific coast in the west across almost to the Atlantic coast in the east, and from British Columbia in the north to New Mexico and Arizona in the south. Its numbers then were about 10 million. The total today is half a million.

The wapiti is larger than a red deer, up to 9 ft long in head and body, 5 ft high at the shoulder and weighing up to 1 000 lb, the hinds being smaller than the stags, as in red deer. It resembles the red deer in colour except that it is less reddish in summer and it has a more prominent light rump patch. Wapiti means 'white deer' and probably refers to this light patch. The antlers of red deer go up to 43 in.; those of wapiti may reach 66 in.

There are four forms of wapiti living in widely differing environments. The largest, living towards the Pacific coast, was named after Theodore Roosevelt in 1897. The smallest, the dwarf or Tule wapiti, lives on the hot, dry plains of southern California. Its coat is much paler than in the other three.

Incompatible neighbours

In spite of the tremendous reductions in its numbers, the wapiti gets in man's way. Most of the half-million survivors are in national parks or other wildlife refuges, mainly in the western states. Two small herds were introduced into the Virginian Jefferson National Forest in the eastern United States, and there have been reintroductions elsewhere. Where they invade arable or other settled land they tend to damage crops or compete with domestic livestock for browse and grazing. They also bark trees, especially the aspen, and wapiti introduced into Australia barked the pokaka. They present the same problem as the red deer in wildlife refuges in Britain; their natural ability to build up numbers under protection is apt to lead to the destruction of their habitat and the need to control them. Regrettably, the hand of man must always be to some extent against the deer in his vicinity.

Musical wapiti

The breeding habits of wapiti are very like those of red deer. There is, however, a marked difference in the stag's calls at the beginning of the rut. Instead of a roar, the wapiti stag makes an undulating bugling which starts in a low key, rises to a high pitch in a prolonged note which abruptly drops to a harsh scream, and ends in a few grunts. Otherwise the details are much the same, with the mature bulls rounding up the hinds into harems in September and October, to the accompaniment of a clatter of antlers and a clashing of foreheads from furious fighting, as the subordinate stags challenge the bulls. In May or June of the following year the hinds leave the herds and go into thickets to drop their dappled calves. There is usually one at a birth, rarely twins and exceptionally triplets, after a gestation of 249–262 days. The calf is up to 30 lb at birth, stands within minutes of being dropped and can run after a few hours. It starts to feed itself at three months, and is weaned and loses its spots in September or October.

Lion-hearted deer

The enemies of wapiti, a prey species itself, are much reduced in numbers at the hands of man. They include wolf, coyote, puma and bear, which prey especially on the calves. Adults can use speed to escape or can turn and defend themselves, striking down with the front hoofs. A big wapiti stag is credited with breaking the back of a wolf with one kick. One wapiti stag reduced a bear to a lacerated carcase with the tines

△ *Wildlife refuges, such as this one beneath the snow-covered Teton Range, harbour most of the American population of wapiti.*

of its antlers, then trampled it furiously until only a battered pulp remained. Such behaviour seems to be unusual until we recall that in the 18th century the Duke of Cumberland, so we are told, had a stag and a tiger brought together in an enclosure and that the stag made 'so bold and furious a defence, that the tiger was at last obliged to give up the contest'.

Dance of the deer

Contemporary accounts tell how the North American Indians sometimes hunted the wapiti in parties, forming a wide crescent around a stag, with the horns of the crescent half a mile apart. As they closed in the stag dashed first one way, then the other until, with the circle closed, the exhausted stag could be taken alive. Nevertheless, unless the animal was completely worn out, he would stand at bay, and usually one or more of the hunters was hurt before the stag was secured. Apparently this 'dance of the deer', as it was called, was for sport. The wapiti stag was also killed by Indians for his upper canine teeth, which were worn as charms. Surprisingly, the carcase was not used but left to rot. Later, some Americans of European origin formed a fraternal order or brotherhood named after this deer, not after its Indian name but after the one wrongly given it by early white settlers, which was 'elk'. Members of the order, it seems, used the canine teeth as emblems, for which a stag was killed, its canines extracted—and the carcase left to rot.

class	**Mammalia**
order	**Artiodactyla**
family	**Cervidae**
genus & species	***Cervus canadensis***

Warbler

There are about 300 warblers, named after the melodious song that is characteristic of many species. They are small, generally 4–5 in. long, with fine-pointed bills, and usually drably coloured, green, brown or grey. Identification is, therefore, not an easy task and many warblers can be identified, even by experienced bird-watchers, only when held in the hand and even then identification can be difficult. Many warblers migrate and because they get blown off course some species turn up in odd places. The appearance of such rarities, together with the difficulties of identification, make the warblers particularly interesting to bird-watchers.

The warblers are sometimes called the Old World warblers to distinguish them from the New World warblers also known as the wood-warblers or American warblers. The two groups are placed in separate families, the Old World warblers having 10 primary flight feathers on each wing and the wood-warblers having only nine. The Old World warblers are very uniform in form and colour, although some tropical warblers are brightly coloured. The sexes usually have similar plumage but they differ in a few cases. For example, the blackcap is an appropriate name only for the male which has a black crown contrasting with the pale grey of the rest of his plumage. The female has a brown cap. Similarly, the Rüppell's warbler has a black head and throat with a white moustache. The female retains the moustache but the head and throat are grey and white.

Warblers are restricted to the Old World except for the Arctic warbler which has crossed the Bering Straits from Siberia to Alaska. The rest are found all over the Old World from western Europe to Australia, with about half in Africa.

Europe having flown southwest when they should have flown southeast.

Warblers have the typical thin, pointed bills of insect eaters and most of them feed entirely on insects, spiders, and the eggs and larvae of insects and other invertebrates, which they find in the bark of trees, in reeds and other plants, and sometimes on the ground. Berries are eaten by some migrating warblers and blackcaps feed at bird-tables during the winter.

Songs gay and dull

Many warblers advertise their presence by elaborate songs that compete in quality with that of the European blackbird, while others have dull songs like that of the grasshopper warbler which can be easily mistaken for the stridulation of a grasshopper. The breeding habits of warblers are fairly uniform. Each pair usually holds a territory and nests in isolation although reed warblers build nests quite close together.

The nests are built near the ground, among bushes, reeds or grasses, and are built of grass or reeds which is woven to form a bowl, ball or even a bottle-shaped nest. The males sometimes build several 'cock nests'. The white, spotted eggs, 3–10 in number, are incubated by the female alone or by both sexes, but both parents usually feed the chicks.

Almost identical twins

Some species of warblers are so similar that it is almost impossible to distinguish them by their plumage. Such species are called sibling or cryptic species and, in the case of warblers, the chiffchaff and willow warbler, among others, are distinguished by their song. The chiffchaff's irregular, high-pitched 'chiff-chaff-chaff-chiff-chaff' is a common sound in the woods during spring whereas the willow warbler has a faint, liquid and regular song repeated at intervals. The breeding range of these two species overlaps in most of Europe but where the willow warbler does not occur, as in Spain and Portugal, the chiffchaff resembles the willow warbler more closely than it does elsewhere. Its legs which are usually noticeably darker than the willow warbler's are lighter in the Iberian peninsula and its song is made up of a pattern of notes rather than the two notes of other chiffchaffs. Presumably the chiffchaff and the willow warbler arose from populations of a common ancestor which became isolated from each other. Now their ranges overlap these differences are sufficient to prevent interbreeding.

Peter Hinchcliffe:Photo Res

◁△ *Male Dartford warbler with his hungry young. He is identified by his slate-grey head, dark brown upper-parts and purplish-brown underparts. This 5in. warbler is constantly cocking and fanning his tail and has rather skulking behaviour. It usually lives on open commons with heather and gorse or on cistus-covered hillsides or dwarf oak trees.*

△ *Chiffchaff fledglings at their nest of moss and dry grass, lined with feathers. They are fed by the female alone and after about 13 days they are able to fly. When adult they look very like willow warblers but their voices clearly identify them; the chiffchaff's song is a monotonous, high-pitched 'chiff-chaff' whereas the willow warbler has a fluent, wistful song.*

◁ *Blackcap family. Its cap—glossy black in the male and red-brown in the female—makes it one of the easiest warblers to identify. Its rich and melodious song has named it 'the northern nightingale'. The frail nest is built in coarse vegetation such as brambles or ever-green shrubs and is attached to the surrounding plants with 'basket handles'.*

Mixed-up migrators

Many warblers spend their lives in one area, while others are migratory, especially those that live in places where the winters are cold. Only 3 of the 13 species breeding in the British Isles spend the winter there. These are the blackcap, chiffchaff and Dartford warbler. Some of the migratory species travel vast distances on their twice yearly journeys: the willow warbler flies up to 7 000 miles, from eastern Siberia to east Africa and the Arctic warbler may travel even farther: from northwest Europe to southeast Asia. The Alaskan population of the Arctic warbler returns to the Old World in the winter, crossing the Bering Straits and flying down to southeast Asia. Sometimes reversed migration takes place and part of a warbler population flies in the opposite direction to the others. This results, for instance, in some warblers arriving in the British Isles in autumn when the others have left. Some Arctic warblers arrive in the British Isles from northern

class	**Aves**
order	**Passeriformes**
family	**Muscicapidae**
genera & species	*Locustella naevia* grasshopper warbler **Phylloscopus collybita** chiffchaff **P. trochilus** willow warbler **Sylvia atricapilla** blackcap **S. undata** Dartford warbler others

Warthog

The warthog is thought by some to have the most grotesque face of all mammals. This is partly because its face is badly proportioned, and partly because of the excrescences or 'warts', strengthened with gristle, on either side of the face. These are prominent in the males only and do not appear to have any function. The male warthog is up to 5 ft long, exclusive of its 18in. tail, stands up to 28 in. at the shoulder and weighs up to 200 lb. The female is somewhat smaller. The skin of both is slate or clay-coloured, with a few bristly hairs over the body and a conspicuous mane of long bristles running from the head down the midline of the back. The most striking feature is, however, the very long head, armed with tusks and ornamented with warts, with the small eyes set well back, only just in front of the ears. The long legs and long head with the stout thick neck make the warthog, when seen standing on all fours and from side view, look like a caricature of a horse. The long thin tail hangs down when the animal moves slowly but is carried stiffly erect with the tufted tip hanging over when it is running.

The curled upper pair of tusks, 12 in. or more in length — the record is 27 in. — are longer than the lower because these bite against only the lower surface of the upper tusks, instead of wearing them away at the points. The upper tusks have enamel at the tips and even this is soon worn away, while the lower tusks are coated with enamel throughout their length. The young warthog has 34 teeth but in the mature adult there may be only eight because the three pairs of lower incisors and one pair of the upper are lost, as well as all the cheek-teeth, except for the last pair of molars. Each of this last pair is large and complex, consisting of a number of long narrow cylindrical denticles, packed closely together.

The warthog is found in most open country in Africa, from Ethiopia to Senegal in the north, southwards to the Orange Free State.

◁ Face to face with ugliness. A male warthog clearly shows its four large and functionless warts — only prominent in males. Despite its ferocious appearance the warthog is basically inoffensive, but when cornered is quite capable of defending itself and its family from the attack of all but the largest and most formidable of predators. Its long upper tusks, with an average length of 1 ft, can inflict severe wounds on the unfortunate enemy.

N Myers: Photo Res

2557

Likes to wallow in mud

Warthogs prefer open thorn bush, thin forest or plains. They feed mainly by day, travelling about singly, in pairs or in family parties of one or two sows with their offspring. The boars are usually solitary. At night they lie up in a den, which may be a cave, a hollow under rocks or a depression they dig in the ground under the shelter of a dense thicket. They wallow in mud, caking their bodies with it, but their dens are kept scrupulously clean. They sometimes use abandoned aardvark burrows for sleeping or as temporary retreats when disturbed. They enter the burrow backwards, presenting their formidable tusks to the entrance, ready to inflict severe wounds on any enemy foolish enough to intrude.

Selective grazer

The warthog is principally a grazer preferring short grass and tender growing tips. The small incisors are used as tweezers to pluck out the selected food. The warthog's neck is too short for comfortable feeding so it goes down on its knees to graze, sometimes shuffling forward in this position. Where water is not available or grass is scarce the warthog may dig up roots. Fruit and berries are also taken and it will very

Sally Anne Thompson

H Klingel

△ *A disinterested Thomson's gazelle passes a family of rooting warthogs. As they have such short necks warthogs drop to their padded knees for more comfortable feeding; they often grunt while rooting but are otherwise rather silent.*

◁ *Warthogs erect their tails only when running.*

occasionally take animal food. During a drought in the Nairobi National Park in 1961 warthogs were frequently seen feeding on the carcases of wildebeest and other animals that had died of hunger or thirst.

The warthog is usually silent but will grunt when feeding. It has a good sense of smell and acute hearing, but poor eyesight.

Rationed piglets

Usually 2—4 young are born from October to November after a gestation of 171—175 days. The warthog sow has only four teats, and recently it has been learned that a litter may number 6. How the meals are arranged is not known. Sows seen suckling their young have been standing, although they may lie down to do so in the burrow when the piglets are first born. The young warthogs are a reddish brown colour.

It is not known how long warthogs live in the wild but one lived in the London Zoo for $12\frac{1}{2}$ years.

Hunted with jeeps

The lion is the warthog's chief enemy in the wild but leopards, cheetahs and wild dogs may take the young ones. Several observers have testified that the warthog is virtually fearless; warthogs have turned and charged pursuing leopards' or elephants, which turned tail and fled. The sow with young is particularly fearless in the defence of her piglets.

Local people hunt the warthog because the flesh is said to be very tasty and today it is hunted with jeeps for sport against which its normal methods of defence and 30 mph maximum speed are of little use.

Odd or misunderstood?

In general each part of an animal's body contributes in some positive way to the welfare of the whole. In most animals there are one or more parts that we speak of as vestigial; they were formerly larger and more vigorous or contributed more to the general economy of the body but are now smaller and are, so to speak, wasting away. Occasionally we find parts that are better labelled rudimentary. These are at their beginning and have not yet developed to the point of playing their full part. Over and above these there are, not infrequently, animal parts, structures and tricks of behaviour which seem to be neither functional, vestigial nor rudimentary. Until we know more about them they may best be described as oddities.

The warthog is one of the oddest of the quadrupeds. Its flat, almost shovel-shaped head, combined with the stout, thick neck, may be useful now, or it may have been useful in the past in perhaps a different kind of habitat, for rooting in the earth or for turning over logs or stones. The warts may possibly serve for additional strength in such exercises. It may be that the warts serve as weapons additional to the tusks, for powerful thrusts at the enemy. If either of these has any truth, there may also be a very good reason why the eyes should be set so far back in the head. This position may keep them out of harm's way when rooting for food. Perhaps this extraordinarily grotesque head would prove, were we better informed on the habits and behaviour of the warthog, to be the result of a combination of remarkable adaptations to a specialised way of life, and oddities only because of our ignorance.

class	**Mammalia**
order	**Artiodactyla**
family	**Suidae**
genus & species	***Phacochoerus aethiopicus***

△ *Meal time: two young warthogs satisfy their appetites while mother feeds on grass. There are usually 2—4 young, sometimes 6. The sow has only four teats, but it is not known how they manage.*
▽ *Quenching their thirst in muddy water; warthogs will often wallow, caking their bodies in mud.*

Wasp

To most people a wasp recalls the black-and-yellow insect often abundant enough in summer to be a nuisance, but in its broader sense the term 'wasp' includes any of the stinging Hymenoptera that is not a bee or an ant.

The common wasp *Vespula vulgaris* and the German wasp *V. germanica* are equally common in Europe, and so alike that the workers are difficult to distinguish, though the queens can be separated by the pattern of their yellow and black markings. Except to entomologists these two are just 'wasps', without any thought of there being more than one species. Almost all that is said here jointly concerns both.

Their nearest European relative is the hornet *Vespa crabro* (p 1111), and they are more distantly related to the paper wasps **Polistes** (p 1692). Their American equivalents, with similar habits, are known colloquially as 'yellowjackets'.

Four other species of *Vespula* are found in Britain, all very similar in appearance to the two common kinds. The red wasp *Vespula rufa* also nests underground, but the tree wasp **V. sylvestris** and the Norwegian wasp **V. norvegica** hang their nests in trees and bushes. Finally there is the cuckoo wasp **V. austriaca** whose queen enters the nest of a red wasp, kills some of the workers and supplants the queen. The parasitic invader's brood is reared by the red wasp workers, the offspring of the parasite consisting entirely of fertile males and females.

▽ Lover of liquids — a wasp feeding.
Adult wasps feed on nectar, fruit and tree sap.

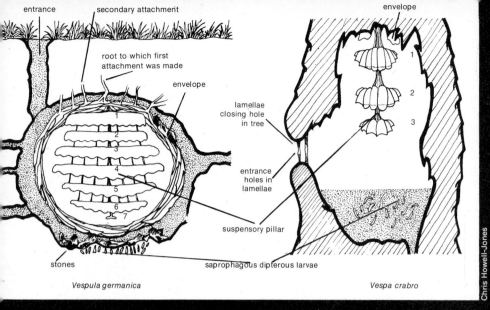

Diagram labels (left, Vespula germanica):
- entrance
- secondary attachment
- root to which first attachment was made
- envelope
- stones
- *Vespula germanica*

Diagram labels (right, Vespa crabro):
- envelope
- lamellae closing hole in tree
- entrance holes in lamellae
- suspensory pillar
- saprophagous dipterous larvae
- *Vespa crabro*

Numerals 1–7 on the comb layers.

Photo credit (vertical): Chris Howell-Jones

The inside story

1. Section through the subterranean nest of the German wasp and a section of a hornets' nest in a tree hollow. The numerals refer to layers of comb in order of construction.

2. Built by a queen: the finely sculptured first cells of the common wasp are suspended by a stalk from a delicate paper canopy.

3. The underside of a layer of cells from the upper story of a common wasps' nest. The white cells contain larvae which prior to pupation spin a cocoon and seal off the mouth of the cell with a layer of tough silk.

4. Whorled and circular design: detail of the outside of a wasps' nest formed by the laborious efforts of the queen. Pieces of wood are rasped with the mandibles, worked up with saliva and masticated to form a substance which when dry has a paper-like consistency.

5. Stratified: section through a common wasps' nest shows the different layers of comb supported by tiny props.

2

3

4

Fear-inflicting German wasp. Wasps usually sting only when annoyed or if their nest is approached.

queen die with the first frosts of autumn.

The workers feed on nectar and fruit juices and also accept drops of liquid exuded by the larvae. The larvae and queen are fed by the workers on the juices of captured insects; wasps destroy great numbers of bluebottle flies.

The larva is a white legless grub and it maintains its position in the upside-down cell by pressing its body against the sides. When fully grown it closes the cell by spinning a papery cover across the mouth. During its life its excrement accumulates at the end of the intestine and is voided all at once in the last larval skin when it changes into a soft white pupa. The wasp emerges 3 – 4 weeks after the eggs were laid.

Guests and parasites
A hoverfly *Volucella* enters wasps' nests and lays its eggs without any interference from the wasps. Its curious prickly larvae play a useful part in the nest as scavangers, living in the midden below the nest, where dirt and dead bodies accumulate, and also entering vacated cells and cleaning out the deposits of excrement. This helps in making the cells available for re-use. The larvae of the moth *Aphomia sociella* also live as scavengers in wasps' nests. Late in the season, when the nest is 'running down', these invade the combs and devour the grubs and pupae. The larva of a rare beetle *Metoecus paradoxus* lives parasitically on the grubs of wasps in underground nests. It is at first an internal parasite (like the larva of an ichneumon (p 1161) or a tachina (p 2345) fly), but later emerges and devours its host. It is a remarkable fact that *Metoecus* apparently invades the nests of only the common wasp, never those of the German wasp, although to our eyes the two species look exactly the same.

The wasp's sting
This formidable weapon is really an ovipositor or egg-laying organ that has become transformed into a tiny hypodermic needle connected with a poison gland. The eggs are extruded from an opening at the base of it. Wasps sting if they are squeezed or restrained, as when they accidentally crawl inside someone's clothing. They also attack and sting if the nest is interfered with or even simply approached. The inhabitants of large, well-populated nests are more aggressive than those of small ones. The two main constituents of the venom are histamine and apitoxin. Old-fashioned remedies such as washing soda and ammonia were based on the mistaken idea that the venom is an acid of some kind, and they are ineffective except in giving reassurance. Genuine relief is given by the application of antihistamine to the site of the sting and by taking antihistamine tablets.

Elaborate paper building
The history of a wasps' nest really begins in the autumn of the year previous to its construction, when the big queen wasps leave the nests where they were hatched, mate and then hide themselves, to pass the winter in hollow trees, sheds and attics. The queen finds a rough beam or piece of sacking, clamps her jaws onto a fibre and hangs unconscious for six or seven months. She emerges in late spring and seeks a crack in the ground or an old mouse's hole running under a tree root. Just below this she digs out a chamber, removing the earth in her jaws. Then she flies repeatedly to and from a fence post or dead tree, each time bringing home a little pellet of paste made by rasping away the wood and moistening the resultant material with saliva. This substance is plastered on to the underside of the root, where it hardens to form a kind of cardboard or paper. A little curved canopy is fixed onto this foundation and a paper stalk is made, pointing down from the centre of the canopy. A cluster of hexagonal cells, also of paper, is then made round the stalk, with their open ends downward. The queen lays an egg in each then encloses this first comb in a bag of paper about as big as a golf ball, with a hole at its lower end.

Building a city
All this time the queen has been feeding on nectar. When the eggs hatch into small white larvae she divides her time between feeding them on the juices of chewed-up insects – they are growing and so require a protein diet – and adding more cells to the comb, enlarging the enclosing bag as she does so. By the time the larvae from the earliest eggs have passed through the pupal stage to produce the first workers, she may have added a storey to her house, built below the first and hanging by little stalks of paper. To make room for the growing nest the queen may have to excavate more earth and carry it away.

When the worker wasps, which are non-reproductive females, appear in quantity, they take over from the queen the job of extending and enlarging their home. New storeys are added, one below the other, increasing to the maximum diameter of the nest and then decreasing again to give it a roughly spherical shape. Quantities of earth are removed by the workers and wood pulp is brought back for construction. The anchorage to the root is strengthened as the bulk and weight of the nest increases, and struts and stays are made between it and the surrounding earth. The queen stays at home, fed by her sexless daughters, who must also bring home animal food for all the growing larvae. As each cell is completed she places an egg in it until a population of as many as 5 000 wasps, or more in very big nests, is built up and maintained. The total number of the queen's offspring that hatch, live and die in the service of the nest throughout a summer may be five times this number.

Make do and mend
When complete the nest is a hollow sphere 8 – 9 in. wide, containing 6 – 10 horizontal combs which extend more or less right across it. The nest is comparable to a house built of bricks and mortar, yet there is a difference: although the nest has a basic external form, the inside is continually being nibbled away and repulped to be added, together with fresh pulp, to the outside and to the expanding combs, so the whole structure is constantly changing.

At the end of the summer a generation of males and functional females is produced. The latter are the queen wasps, similar to workers but larger; the males are about the same size as the workers but have much longer antennae. Eggs which produce workers and queens are always fertilised by spermatozoa from the store which the queen acquired at mating and keeps in her body. Males are produced from unfertilised eggs, from which the queen withholds sperm as she lays them. After mating the males soon die and the queens hibernate. At the end of the summer the workers become lazy and cease to maintain the economy of the nest, and they and the old

phylum	**Arthropoda**
class	**Insecta**
order	**Hymenoptera**
family	**Vespidae**

Water beetle

Fresh water would not remain fresh for long if it were not for scavengers like the water beetles that feed on decaying vegetation. There are 2 000 species in the worldwide family, most numerous in the tropics, known as water beetles, or sometimes as water scavenger beetles, to avoid confusion with another family, the diving beetles (p 643). The name is not wholly appropriate because not all species live in water, some living in damp places among vegetable rubbish, others in dung.

Many water beetles look very like the diving beetles because both are dark brown or black and oval in outline. The former are, however, stouter, less flat, and differ in their habits, especially in the way they swim and breathe. The silver water beetle is one of the best known and largest. It is nearly 2 in. long, black and smooth above. Under water it appears bright silvery underneath due to a covering of very fine short hairs which trap a thin layer of air. Usually hidden under the head, the antennae are short and clubbed, and are used in breathing. There are much-elongated palps on the maxillae which look like a second pair of antennae, and in many species these function as such.

Awkward swimmers

Water beetles live in shallow weedy ponds, in pools in marshes, some mainly on damp land, a few live in brackish water or in running water where there are plenty of algae. They swim awkwardly with alternate strokes of the legs, very different from the efficient rowing action of more truly aquatic beetles such as the great diving beetles. The first pair of legs are not adapted to swimming and the beetle uses first the middle and hindlegs of one side, then those of the other. These are flattened and fringed. When the silver water beetle submerges it carries a silvery film of air on the underside and a bubble between the body and wing-cases. The beetle replenishes its store in a peculiar way, coming to the surface headfirst, not tail first like the diving beetles,

turning on one side and piercing the surface film with one of the antennae. This forms a funnel which puts the outside air in continuity with the two stores of air the beetle carries. This species, like other members of the family, also flies at night and is attracted to artificial light.

The adult beetle feeds on water plants, including algae, or on decaying matter, seldom on living animal prey, although the larvae are more often predatory. Where the larvae live in dung they are maggot-like, feeding on fly maggots found there. In some parts of the Far East water beetles are used to combat the larvae of other beetles which damage sugar cane and banana stems.

Carnivorous larvae

The female silver water beetle spins a large silken cocoon and attaches it to the underside of a leaf of floating vegetation. A vertical 'chimney' projects above the water surface, allowing air to reach the 50–100 eggs laid inside. Sometimes the cocoons are spun independently of any support and they float like small brown balloons at the surface, with the chimney looking like a mast. In a

few species the female carries the cocoon about with her, held between her hindlegs. When these hatch the larvae swallow some air and then bite their way out of the cocoon. The object of swallowing the air seems to be to make the larvae buoyant so they can rise to the surface to breathe. Unlike the adults they are carnivorous, but confine their attentions mainly to water snails. The jaws are asymmetrical and are apparently designed for holding and cutting through the shell of a snail. Well-grown larvae also prey on tadpoles. The soft body of the prey is eaten normally, not externally digested as in the case of the diving beetle larva.

The larva is nearly 3 in. long when fully grown. At this time it leaves the water to pupate in an earthen cell.

An aquarium favourite

It is not surprising that such a large, handsome and well-behaved insect as the silver water beetle should be a favourite with aquarium keepers. It is rather rare and in Britain is mainly confined to the south. At one time it was thought that over-collecting

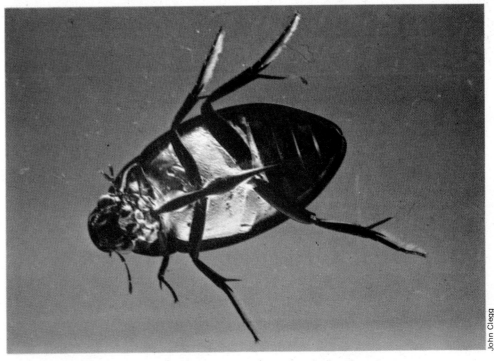

The silver water beetle, so-called because of the shiny layer of air on its underside.

John Clegg

▽ *Bottom up: diving beetle* **Dysticus** *fills the air reservoir trapped behind its wing cases.*

▽ *Antennae raised, water beetle* **Octhebius** *renews the air store under its body.*

△ *The silver water beetle, so-called because of the shiny layer of air on its underside.*

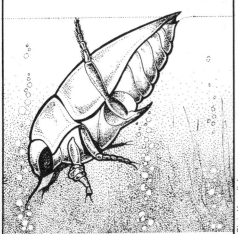

Chris Howell-Jones

Chris Howell-Jones

for aquaria was a threat to its existence. This is probably no longer the case, but it is now in far greater danger than before from modern agricultural operations involving filling up ponds and the mechanical dredging of drainage ditches in country that was formerly marshland. This, added to the way the beetles or their larvae serve as food for birds, fish, frogs and toads, may be too much for the water beetles.

phylum	**Arthropoda**
class	**Insecta**
order	**Coleoptera**
family	**Hydrophilidae**
genus & species	***Hydrous (=Hydrophilus) piceus*** *others*

Waterbuck

The waterbuck is a large antelope which is always found near rivers but which, in spite of its name, lives on drier ground than the closely related kob (p 1254) and lechwe (p 1295). It is 48–53 in. high and may weigh 450–500 lb. It has a coarse, rough, brownish coat, blackish feet and white on the midline of the underparts round the muzzle and round the eyes. There is also an indistinct white band round the neck behind the ears, and either a white ring round the rump or a white patch in that region. The neck and haunches of adult males are thick, and some have a shaggy mane down the throat. Only the males have horns and these are long and slender, ribbed all the way up, and make a smooth crescentic path out and back, then in and forward. They do not have an 'elbow' halfway up the horn like a kob or a lechwe.

Waterbuck are found over most of Africa south of the Sahara. One type with a white rump-patch is known as the defassa or singsing and is found in the more westerly parts of the range. The second type with the white ring known as the common waterbuck, is found more to the east. At one time the two were considered different species but it is now known that they interbreed where their ranges meet. Thus, in parts of East Africa such as the Nairobi National Park, the herds cannot be definitely classed as one species or the other, but show all intermediates between the white patch and the white ring forms. South of the East African parts of their range they are separated by geographical barriers; in Zambia, their ranges are divided by the Muchinga escarpment, and further south by desert. Moreover, each type shows geographic variation, and there are altogether about seven subspecies of waterbuck: three of the common and four defassa, differing among themselves in colour, the amount of white round the eye, length of ear and other details.

H Klingel

△ A horned male common waterbuck will try to keep a female which strays into his territory.

▽ Females and young move about in groups during the day, grazing their home ranges.

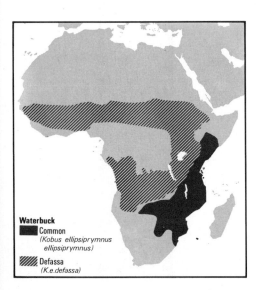

Waterbuck

■ Common
(Kobus ellipsiprymnus ellipsiprymnus)

▨ Defassa
(K.e.defassa)

Protection in darkness

Waterbuck live in the savannah zone, even in somewhat arid country, but always near water. Thus they are found in the savannahs of southern Gabon, which they have invaded across the Congo river from the south—not by penetrating the forest belt from the north. In the arid country of Somalia they are restricted to the major river valleys. The thick cover by the rivers gives them protection. They come out to graze in the grassland beyond, returning again to rest. They are basically diurnal, and where they have not been hunted, as in the Nairobi Park, they stay in the grasslands all day and return to cover at dusk. Where they have been constantly shot at and disturbed, as in the Congo and Somalia, they come out at night and lie up during the day. This is an interesting example of the way an animal's habits may change under human pressure.

Territorial status

A male waterbuck holds a territory covering between ¼ and 1 square mile, extending along the river and back into the grazing areas. He moves about daily to and from the riverine thickets within the territory, the boundaries of which are clearly defined by the owner's behaviour, at least along the river, although less clearly further inland. The length of its river frontage is an indication of the rank of the male holding it.

The male tries to attract females into his territory. Should a group of females wander through it he tries to keep them, while his neighbours move up to the boundary ready to herd the females the moment they move out. The male herds the females by running in front of them and standing with his head up and forefeet together, thus blocking their path, and while they are moving he will give chase, running alongside and butting them.

The females have their own home ranges, which are used for grazing. They are similar in extent to a male's territory, but are not defended. A group of females may therefore move unchallenged into a neighbouring group's home range, and out again as occasion demands. The home ranges, moreover, cut across the males' territories, so the females are constantly harassed as they wander to graze. They spend the night with their young in the riverside bush in groups of three or four. During the day they move about the home ranges in larger groups of up to 30. A few subadult males move along with the females, but those past puberty are usually evicted by the territory-owners, and they join a peripheral herd until each can set up a territory of his own.

Greeting ceremonies

When a male greets a female he sniffs and licks her vulva and tail or else he adopts the *flehmen* pose—head raised, lips drawn back, nose wrinkled—and then he uses the *laufschlag*, stroking between the female's leg or under her belly with his foreleg. He then mounts the female without necessarily mating. A male will graze alongside females he has attracted into his territory and occasionally perform a greeting ceremony with them. A female in season will move a greater distance and graze for a longer time each day than one who is not. She therefore passes through the territories of a greater number of males and the greeting ceremony is more complex than usual. The male may, for example, rub against the female with his face and the base of his horns, where there is a depression, richly supplied with nerves. He will often put his horns on either side of her rump and push slightly.

Gestation takes 240 days, the single young being born in riverside cover. At first the mother leaves the thicket later in the day and returns earlier than the females without young, leaving her young for as short a time as possible. Later, after 3–4 weeks, the young begins to come into the open. Although the sex ratio is thought to be about equal at birth, only 30% of the adult population are males.

Harmonious feeding

Waterbuck and the related kob and lechwe occupy the same terrain in the National Park on the borders of Botswana and Southwest Africa, but they do not compete for food. To begin with, the three species differ in their food preferences at different times of year. Lechwe prefer young grasses, eating the newly emergent perennials in May and the grasses sprouting after the burnings in December. Kob—in this case the subspecies known as puku—prefer somewhat more matured grasses, and so although they eat the same foods as lechwe it is in different proportions, and somewhat later in the year. Waterbuck like matured grasses, and during the floods may often be seen standing up to their bellies in water, having left the dry ridges to feed on the exposed portions of mature plants. Annuals which sprout in January are grazed to a great extent only by lechwe. In this way three large species of very closely related antelope can share the same habitat.

class	**Mammalia**
order	**Artiodactyla**
family	**Bovidae**
genus & species	*Kobus ellipsiprymnus defassa* defassa *K. e. ellipsiprymnus* common waterbuck

Nolly Zaloumis

Water-holding frog

Any frog or toad is likely to discharge a fluid from its bladder when gently squeezed, and this fluid is mainly water. Frogs and toads living in deserts hold more water in their bladders and are therefore termed water-carrying or water-holding. One more especially has been singled out for this name: the water-holding frog of the deserts of Australia.

It is squat-bodied, 2½ in. long, with fairly short, stout front legs and plump hindlegs with webbed toes. It is greenish-grey, often with a dark line down the middle of the back, and its skin is warty. The head seems small for the bloated body; the animal looks more like the European common toad than the common frog. This may be why this and other similar species in Australia have at times been called water-holding or water-carrying toads.

The range of the water-holding frog covers the dry areas of New South Wales and Queensland, northern South Australia and Central Australia.

places are in the heart of the continent, where the annual rainfall is less than 5 in. a year. In this area, however, the rain falls as heavy but infrequent showers, and in a given district there may be a lapse of several years between one rainstorm and the next. During periods of drought the water-holding frog lies buried, as much as 3 ft down in the ground, where the soil is permanently moist. It also lays down a skin-bag or 'cocoon' around itself, by casting off the cell-deep outer layer of its skin. This is separated from it except at the nostrils, and water accumulates between the skin and the skin-bag, which inhibits evaporation. The frog remains so, in a torpid state, eating nothing, until the next rainstorm. Then it casts off the skin-bag and comes to the surface to feed rapidly on insects that become abundant during the wet spell. At the same time the frog replenishes its water supply and breeds.

Brief infancy

The frogs breed in the temporary pools caused by the heavy rains, in the same way as pond-breeding frogs and toads everywhere (see p 496). The main difference is that the eggs hatch in much less than the usual time and the tadpoles develop much

It seems reasonable to suppose, however, that the main hazards in the life of water-holding frogs are connected with the very brief period of infancy. When so much development, feeding and water storage must be carried through in so short a space of time there must be many tadpoles and froglets that fail to make the grade. It may also be shown in due course that there is predation, by birds and reptiles principally, while the frogs are above ground. That such enemies are few may, however, be inferred from the large populations of this and other desert amphibians known to exist, not only in Australia but in other deserts, as in the southwest United States.

Food and drink in one

In fact, some water-holding frogs and toads occur outside Australia but these have received less notice than their Australian relatives. This is partly because their adaptations are less extreme, but it is due more to the link between the amphibians and the Aborigines of Australia. We are told that when the Aborigine feels thirsty he digs a water-holding amphibian out of the ground, holds it over his open mouth and squeezes it to quench his thirst. This is, it seems, an over-simplification. Harry Frauca, in his *Book of Australian Wild Life*, tells us that water-holding frogs are 'said to be found in large numbers in the claypans of Centralia and to provide some aborigines with food and drink. There are reports to the effect that some tribes will dig up Water-holding Frogs from the claypans, squash them and drink the liquid contained inside the bodies and later on throw the frogs into the cookpot'.

Amphibians re-defined

Frogs and toads belong to the class Amphibia, the name meaning loosely 'animals leading double lives'. We tend, therefore, to think of them as spending half their time in water and half on land. In fact, some like the clawed toad spend all their time in water. At the other extreme there are many which never go into water, including the Stephens Island frog of New Zealand, 80 different kinds in New Guinea and adjacent islands and four in Australia. All of them, when not in water, must live in moist places, where evaporation from the skin can be counterbalanced by intake of water through the skin, or else must take their water supply around with them. Amphibians are therefore not so much animals spending half their time in water and half out, but animals adapted to ensuring to themselves a supply of water whether they are immersed in it or outside it. When outside it, however, the desert-living amphibians can lose water equal to a third of their body weight without necessarily dying.

Tanker frogs

Frogs and toads can lose water rapidly through their skin, but they can also rapidly absorb water through it, which is why they never drink. Most of this water is stored in the lymph spaces under the skin and between the muscles. Much of it is stored in the bladder and can be taken back into the rest of the body if needed. What this means can best be appreciated by comparing the clawed toad (p 451) of Africa with the water-holding frog. The clawed toad continually lives in water and has a small bladder capable of holding only 1% of its body weight. The bladder of the water-holding frog can hold up to 50% of its body weight in water.

Cocooned for the dry spell

The climate map of Australia shows that over half the surface of the continent has 10 in. or less of rain each year. The driest

△ *Fat frog:* **Cyclorana australis** *is adapted to living in the more arid regions of Australia.*

more quickly. They become froglets in less than a fortnight, compared with, for example, the 10 weeks taken by the European common frog to reach the same stage. The young frogs feed heavily and rapidly and also fill up with water, then they bury themselves in the ground before the hot sun dispels the moisture remaining from the heavy rainfall.

Speed kills

It is hardly surprising that little precise information is available on many aspects of the biology of animals living under such rigorous conditions. It is only within recent years that a few of the animals in deserts near the more densely populated regions of the world, where biologists are more numerous, have been subjected to close scrutiny.

class	**Amphibia**
order	**Salientia**
family	**Leptodactylidae**
genus & species	***Cyclorana platycephalus*** *others*

△ Predacious pair: water scorpions in weeds.

Heather Angel

△ Diagonally placed: water stick insect with legs and breathing siphon extended is about 2 in. long.

A Klots

Water scorpion

Water scorpions are bugs and therefore have nothing to do with the more familiar land scorpions, and they are far less dangerous to people. They are water insects, called scorpions because of the shape of their front legs, which are modified for grasping prey, and the presence of a long, slender 'tail', which resembles to a very slight degree a scorpion's tail. The larger kinds of water scorpion can pierce the human skin with their beaks with painful but not serious effects. In Australia people are attacked often enough to have earned for the insects the name 'toe-biter' or 'needle bug'.

Water scorpions are flat, blackish-brown insects, the largest being no more than 1—2 in. long. They live on the bottom around the edges of muddy ponds and ditches and are difficult to see on account of their resemblance to water-logged dead leaves. The more or less oval outline of the body is made more leaf-like because the 'tail' looks so like a leaf-stalk. They are poor swimmers and seldom venture into open water, but may climb about on water weeds to get to the surface to breathe air. For this they use the tail, which consists of two half-tubes closely applied to each other and held together by interlocking bristles to form a 'snorkel', the tip of which is pushed above the surface.

The family which includes the water scorpions is a small one, with only about 150 species, but these are well distributed over the world. The water stick insect is in the same family.

Wings hide evolutionary secrets

When the wing-cases of a water scorpion are raised a pair of very delicate hind-wings are revealed. These are never used, however, as the insect has lost some of the principal wing muscles and cannot fly. The wings are pink with bright red veins and the part of the hind body over which they lie is brick-red with black bands. This permanently concealed splendour must have had a function at some time, so it must be supposed that this loss of the use of the wings has occurred rather recently in its evolutionary history. Another feature that is revealed when the wings are lifted is a group of three pairs of false spiracles on the surface of the abdomen below the wings. The spiracles of insects are primarily breathing pores, but in the water scorpion only those at the base of the breathing tube are used for this. The three pairs on the upper surface of the abdomen are balancing organs. Experiments have shown that these spiracles are extremely sensitive to water pressure, which will be very slightly greater on the side of the insect which is tilted downwards from the horizontal position.

Predacious bugs

Water scorpions are predatory, seizing small tadpoles, insects and other animals with their forelegs, each of which is hinged like a clasp knife, so the end portion can fold back into a groove along the basal part. The piercing beak, a feature characteristic of the whole order Hemiptera—bugs— is plunged into the victim, which is killed and consumed by external digestion. In this type of feeding digestive juice is pumped down the beak and into the victim, thus dissolving the tissues, which are then sucked back in liquid form. As well as being digestive the injected juice is also poisonous and quickly paralyses and kills the prey—even large victims, like young fish, are quickly subdued.

Chains of eggs

Water scorpions lay their eggs in spring, among aquatic plants near the surface. At one end of each egg is a bunch of seven long filaments. These become entangled and the eggs cling to each other in chains. The newly-hatched young are like their parents, except in size.

Means to an end

Water stick insects are larger than most water scorpions. They are long and slender with long legs, rather like the familiar stick insects after which they are named. The breathing siphon is nearly as long again as the rest of the body, which is light ochreous in colour, and its mode of feeding is similar to that of the water scorpion. Water stick insects live in still waters among water weeds and standing reeds. Unlike water scorpions they have functional wings and will fly in search of a new habitat if their pond or ditch dries up. Their eggs are most peculiar. They are inserted into floating leaves, such as those of water lilies, the female having a saw-like ovipositor for cutting the leaves and fixing the eggs in position.

Perhaps the most remarkable thing about this unusual family is that the two types of insects have come to look like vegetation. One has come to look like leaves, the other like stems, and all within the one family.

phylum	**Arthropoda**
class	**Insecta**
order	**Hemiptera**
suborder	**Heteroptera**
family	**Nepidae**
genera & species	***Nepa cinerea*** *water scorpion* ***Ranatra linearis*** *water stick insect*

Water shrew

A water shrew swimming underwater has been likened to an 'animated air-bubble' due to the air trapped in its fur, which gives the submerged body a silvery appearance. It is larger than the common shrew (p 2129), the head and body being 3–3¾ in. and the tail about 3 in. long. The body looks bulky but an adult weighs no more than ½ oz, even less in winter. The upper parts vary from a slaty black to dark brown and the light ash-grey or dirty white of the underparts, sharply separated from the upper, appear pure white by contrast. The water shrew's snout is short and broad and its eyes small and blue. The ears, each bearing a tuft of white hairs, are entirely hidden beneath the fur. The feet are brown and broad, the hindfeet—usually more than ¾ in.— being the longer. The toes are bordered with stiff hairs which make them efficient paddles. They are also used in grooming the fur. The tapering tail of the adult water shrew, flattened from side to side, has a double fringe of strong silvery-grey hairs along its underside, constituting a

F Greenaway: NHPA

keel and making the guiding tail more efficient as a rudder.

It is mainly the difference in dentition that has caused the water shrew to be placed in a separate genus from the other shrews. Although the teeth have coloured tips like the others, the points of the incisors are more hooked and there are two less teeth than in other species.

The water shrew is found through most of Europe and southwest and northern Asia. In southern Europe and Asia Minor it is replaced by the closely-related Mediterranean water shrew, which is slightly smaller with the upperparts a slightly paler brown, and it lacks the keel of hairs on the underside of the tail. In the British Isles it is widely distributed throughout England, Wales and Scotland but is not found in Ireland, the Isle of Man, the Outer Hebrides, Orkneys or Shetlands.

Two species in North America, the northern water shrew and the Pacific water shrew, are very similar to the European water shrew. They range from Alaska south to California and eastwards to southeast Canada and northeastern United States.

P Morris

2570

Jane Burton: Photo Res

Jane Burton: Photo Res

△ *Rudder and keel: the water shrew* **Neomys**
fodiens *is well equipped for aquatic hunting.*
It can swim and dive well, using its fringed
toes as paddles, sometimes walking on the
bottom of streams. The long tapering tail,
flattened from side to side, is an effective
rudder and its silver-grey fringe on the under-
side acts as a keel.
◁△ *Hungry hunter: a water shrew devours a*
stickleback with all possible speed.
◁ *A water shrew must hunt at food for 2—3*
hourly periods to survive.

Walking on the bottom

Water shrews live on the banks of streams,
rivers or lakes. They are more active by
day than by night, with alternating periods
of feeding and rest slightly longer than
those of the common shrew. They seldom
venture more than a couple of yards from
the bank, swimming buoyantly with the
head slightly above the surface and the
body flattened. Water shrews appear to be
able to walk for a time along the bottom
of a stream, and at other times they make
distinct leaps out of the water, presumably
after flying insects. Their range of vision
is limited, so a water shrew is readily
alarmed only by sudden noises.

They make shallow burrows in a bank for
sleeping quarters but there is no hibernation; in winter shrews may even be seen
chasing their prey beneath the ice.

It always comes as a surprise to people to
find a water shrew miles from the nearest
river or lake, and it is not yet settled whether
these are resident in such places or whether
their presence there is transitory. Normally
the water shrew has a home range of up to
60 yd, but live-trapping experiments made
within the last few years have shown that
some mammal species include residents, the
majority, which keep to a home range, and
transients, that seem to be more nomadic.

It may be that water shrews found far from
water are transients, or merely wanderers.

The water shrew has a cricket-like chirp,
near the upper limit of the human ear,
audible to young persons but inaudible to
the elderly, as with the squeaks of bats.

A poisonous bite

Whirligig beetles and water gnats on the
surface are chased by water shrews and at
the bottom the shrews search for caddis
worms and other insect larvae. They eat a
variety of other aquatic animals such as
snails, worms, small crustaceans, frogs and
small fishes. They are not averse to carrion.
Water shrews have also been caught in
traps baited with cheese. Their bite is
poisonous, and tests have shown that a
secretion from their submaxillary glands
can be lethal even to small rodents.

Short life span

The breeding season in the British Isles is
from mid-April to September with a peak
in May or June. The female burrows farther
into the bank than for the sleeping quarters
and the nursery is a small chamber lined
with moss and fine roots, or there may be
a round nest of woven grass or leaves. After
a gestation of 24 days, 5—8 blind and naked
young are born, each weighing just over
$\frac{1}{30}$ oz. They develop rapidly, are weaned in
27 days and are independent at 5—6 weeks
old. There is probably a second litter in
September. The water shrew's life span is
only about 15 months and most of them die
well before this.

Many enemies

The chief enemies of the water shrew are
owls, but they are probably taken by stoats,
weasels, vipers and smooth snakes. Many
more fall victim to the larger predatory
fishes such as pike, eels and large trout.

Grooming over breakfast

As has already been said, water shrews have
alternating periods of feeding and resting;
a shrew without food for 2—3 hours will
certainly die of starvation.

The water shrew is even worse off than
other shrews in that, although it is an aquatic
animal, it cannot stay long in water because
it cannot stand long periods of exposure
to cold. As soon as it has grabbed some food
in the water it comes out onto the bank. It
runs through the tunnel it has made in the
bank to squeeze the water out of its fur, then
it combs the fur to get rid of any water left,
using its hindfeet, which are fringed with
bristles and act as combs. If it did not
immediately do this the waterlogged fur
would cause it to lose heat even more
rapidly and it would quickly die of cold. Not
only does a water shrew eat its own weight
of food in 24 hours, but it does what probably no other animal needs to do: it continues to eat while grooming its fur. Most
animals have a meal and then groom themselves but a water shrew cannot afford to
waste time in this way.

class	**Mammalia**
order	**Insectivora**
family	**Soricidae**
genera & species	**Neomys fodiens** *water shrew* **N. anomalus** *Mediterranean water shrew* **Sorex bendirii** *Pacific water shrew* **S. palustris** *northern water shrew* *others*

Looped on a log—a common water snake. This handsomely marked North American snake is a close relative of the European grass snake.

Water snake

The name water snake is likely to be given to any snake that spends most of its life in or near water feeding on aquatic animals. Most water snakes belong to the family Colubridae, but those that have the best claim to the name have recently been given a family of their own, the Acrochordidae. They live on the coasts from India to the Solomon Islands and are nearly as well adapted to aquatic life as the sea snakes. The largest, **Acrochordus javanicus,** *sometimes known as the elephant's trunk snake, grows up to 6 ft in the largest females. The nostrils are on the top of the snout and can be tightly closed by muscular valves. The body is streamlined, as the scales are placed edge to edge rather than overlapping. For this reason these Oriental water snakes are used as snakeskin leather for shoes and handbags.*

A very widespread group of water snakes belong to the genus **Natrix,** *including the grass snake (p 934) of Europe. These water snakes are found in North America, Europe, North Africa and Asia as far east as the East Indies and can be regarded as one of the most successful and abundant of the non-poisonous snakes. There are about 75 species, most living in the Orient, 10 in North America and three in Europe, two of which have spread into North Africa. In appearance these water snakes are 'typical snakes', with fairly slender heads. The scales are ridged and rarely brightly coloured. The common water snake of North America* **Natrix sipedon,** *however, has red-brown bands or spots on its back with a white or yellow belly with bright red dots. This snake is also called the northern banded water snake or moccasin, but it should not be confused with the deadly water moccasin* **Agkistrodon piscivorus,** *a pit viper.*

In Africa south of the Sahara there are several water snakes, including the olive-brown water snake **Lycodonomorphus rufulus** *and the olive water snake* **Natriciteres olivacea,** *which rarely exceed a length of 1 ft, and the black-bellied water snake* **Hydraethiops melanogaster** *of the rain forests. In the Orient there are also the mountain water snakes* **Opisthotropis,** *and in the Orient, Australian and Pacific regions there are the rear-fanged water snakes of the sub-family Homalopsinae.*

Evil defensive odours

Water snakes are either non-poisonous or, as in the rear-fanged water snakes (p 1922), only mildly so. When disturbed they escape by diving into water, but if cornered the water snakes of the genus *Natrix* will turn and attack. The common American water snake, which may grow up to 4 ft, flattens its body and strikes, sometimes drawing blood. No venom is injected but there is a danger of blood poisoning if the wound is not cleaned. The final line of defence is to emit an evil-smelling liquid.

The common American water snake lives in marshes, streams and lakes but, like other water snakes, spends much of its time sunning itself draped over branches overhanging water. Other *Natrix* water snakes are less attracted to the water and may often be found on land some distance from water. The Oriental water snakes, on the other hand, are extremely specialised. They are almost helpless on land and live exclusively in rivers and estuaries, sometimes swimming along the coast.

Fishes and frogs

The diet of water snakes is largely fishes or amphibians. The *Natrix* water snakes, in particular, feed largely on frogs, but the chequered water snake *Natrix tessellata* of Central Europe feeds mainly on fishes and is more aquatic in its habits than its frog-eating relatives. The black-bellied water snake of Africa is also a fish-eater and the dog-faced snake *Cerberus rhynchops* pursues mudskippers (p 1526) overland. It is sometimes caught by anglers.

Varied breeding

There is a wide variety in the breeding habits of water snakes. The wholly aquatic Oriental water snakes bear their young alive. About 30 are born in each brood without the mother's having to come ashore. The American *Natrix* water snakes are also ovoviviparous which may, again, be related to their aquatic habits; the European water snakes, which are less aquatic, lay eggs.

Defences foiled

The olive-brown water snake of Africa feeds mainly on frogs, their tadpoles and occasional small fishes. Frogs have an admirable escape mechanism in their ability to jump 10 – 15 ft, and no doubt many a water snake has missed its meal through a timely jump by a frog. On the other hand, frogs are undoubtedly caught by water snakes. Dr Vincent Wager, an authority on African reptiles, has suggested that water snakes catch frogs as they come ashore into dense vegetation where only short jumps are possible. The snake chases the frog, grabs it by one leg then quickly throws a number of coils around its body. When the frog is properly trussed up, the snake manoeuvres its mouth over the frog's head.

Another water snake that overcomes its prey's defensive equipment is the common water snake of North America which eats catfish, ignoring the fin spines, although they may sometimes pierce the gut wall.

class	**Reptilia**	
order	**Squamata**	
suborder	**Serpentes**	
families	**Acrochordidae** **Colubridae**	

Water spider

Although many spiders can live temporarily underwater, or even voluntarily enter water, there is only one species that lives more or less permanently below the surface. It does so by constructing a diving bell.

There is nothing unusual about the appearance of the water spider. It is small-bodied and long-legged, the front part of the body light brown with faint dark markings, the chelicerae reddish brown and the abdomen greyish and covered with rather short hairs. An unusual feature is that the females are usually smaller than the males, the size range being 8–15 mm although females of up to 28 mm long—just over an inch—have been recorded.

The water spider ranges across temperate Europe and Asia.

▽ A male water spider, usually larger than a female, crawls over some water vegetation. Only the **Argyroneta** species of spiders spend their entire life in the water.

Stocking up with air

Although it lives permanently in water, the water spider is dependent on air for breathing. It rises to the surface and hangs head-down from the surface film with the end of its abdomen pushed up into the air. With a sudden jerk of the abdomen and the hind pair of legs a bubble of air is trapped on the spider's underside. The spider then descends, swimming down or climbing down the stems of water plants, to its thimble-shaped bell of silk, holding the bubble of air between its hindlegs. It enters and, with its head directed towards the top of the bell, the bubble of air slides forward under the spider and the front part of it is released, to rise to the top of the bell. The spider then turns round, directing the tip of the abdomen upwards, and releases the rest of the air, stroking the abdomen with the rear legs if necessary to brush it off. The spider then goes to the surface and swims down with another silver bubble, this being repeated until the bell is filled with air.

Building the bell

The bell is made by first spinning a platform of silk between the stems or leaves of water plants, with strands running out from the spider to the vegetation around. Wherever the spider goes it lays down a guide line of silk and this may serve other purposes than guiding the spider back to its home. The thread accumulation probably helps to secure the silken bell, and insects bumping into them probably alert the spider to the approach of prey. Once the platform of silk has been spun the spider releases air beneath it, making the silk web bulge upwards. As more and more air is added the web takes on the shape of a bell or thimble.

Lying in ambush

During the day the spider remains inside the bell, with the front legs pushed beyond the mouth of the bell, into the water. Any small animal, particularly an insect or its larva, passing near will make the spider dash out, seize it and return to the bell to eat it. An insect falling on the surface of the water will also set up vibrations to which the spider is sensitive, sending it to the surface to seize the insect and take it down to the bell to be eaten. By night the spider leaves its bell to hunt, but it will always return to the bell with its prey.

Aviating submariners

Mating begins in spring or early summer with the male loading his palps with sperm and setting out to visit a female in her bell. If she is ready to mate only a brief courtship ensues, otherwise she lunges at him, making him retire. Having mated with her he may remain in her bell for a while and even mate a second time. The female lays 50–100 eggs in a silken bag that takes up the upper half of the cavity of the bell. The eggs hatch in 3–4 weeks, the spiderlings biting their way through the bag into the bell where they stay for a few weeks, moulting twice during that time. Some of the brood stay in the same pond, but many go to the surface, climb out, spin threads of silk onto the wind and float away – to find a new pond or die.

Predators preyed upon

There is probably a heavy mortality as the young spiders disperse. Even after this stage of the life cycle has been safely passed, enemies are numerous. They include dragonfly larvae, backswimmers, water stick insects, beetles and their larvae, frogs, fish and possibly larger members of their own species. Whether cannibalism occurs in the wild or is, as so often has been demonstrated, the result of being in captivity, would be hard to say.

As winter approaches, water spiders go to a lower level in the pond and spin a winter bell, stocking it with air. Some will use an empty water snail shell lying on the bottom. The one bubble of air will last 4–5 months, since the spider is completely immobile and using almost no energy while in its submerged winter quarters.

Ten minutes' grace

Among other spiders that voluntarily submerge in water, one species has been tested experimentally. It is unrelated to the water spider, belonging to the family Pisauridae, and is named *Dolomedes triton*. WH McAlister, of the University of Texas, found that this spider requires a solid surface to push itself into and out of the surface film, and while submerged needs a solid support to cling to as an anchor. So it is fair to say that the spider deliberately enters water. In addition it was found to remain submerged voluntarily for 4–9 minutes, exceptionally up to 30 minutes. While being tested it was found to survive sustained immersion for up to 180 minutes, which is 10 times as long as most terrestrial spiders.

People often find a spider in the bath. Many are strongly averse to spiders yet are equally averse to killing one, so solve the problem by washing it down the wastepipe. They often ask – having perpetrated the foul deed – whether the spider dies from this. Most spiders tend to trap some air among the hairs on their bodies when immersed, and from McAlister's experiments it would seem that most spiders can stand up to 10 minutes' immersion, some can stand more than this, which should give them time to get out of the water to safety – provided the water used to wash them away is not hot.

▽ *A water spider inside its bell of air, which is still in the early stage of construction.*

John Clegg

phylum	**Arthropoda**
class	**Arachnida**
order	**Araneae**
family	**Agelenidae**
genus & species	*Argyroneta aquatica*

Terra cotta trio: a family of water voles around the entrance to their burrow—made up of sleeping and food-storage chambers connected by tunnels.

John Markham

Water vole

The water vole is apt to suffer from its folkname of 'water rat'. It is about the size of the common rat and can be easily mistaken for it, yet generally speaking cannot even be called a nuisance. Head and body total $7\frac{1}{2}-8\frac{1}{2}$ in, and the tapering and hairy ringed tail is about $4\frac{1}{2}$ in long. Its weight varies from $3\frac{3}{4}-5\frac{3}{4}$ oz in winter to almost double this in summer. The females are slightly smaller than the males. The head is short and thick with a broad and rounded muzzle. The eyes are small and extremely short-sighted, and the small round ears scarcely project beyond the surrounding fur. The limbs are relatively short and the feet, which are not webbed, are naked, pale pink on the underside with five rounded pads, and clothed with stiff hairs on the upper surface. All the toes are well clawed. The long, thick, glossy fur varies from a blackish-grey to a warm reddish-brown above, sprinkled with grey, and the under-parts are yellowish-grey. The female's fur is more chestnut. A few black melanistic forms are found, as are albino strains.

The water vole is found over most of Europe, parts of Russia and Siberia, Asia Minor, northern Syria, Israel and Iran. It is generally distributed throughout Britain, but does not occur in Ireland or on the Scottish islands. In many parts of its range outside Britain it lives entirely on land, burrowing rather like a mole.

Diving to safety

The water vole is found on the banks of streams, rivers and canals. It is thought to have a four-hourly rhythm of activity throughout the day and night, with feeding periods of about half an hour alternating with periods of rest or random movement. There is, however, disagreement among those who have studied the water vole; some describe it as mainly nocturnal. If the latter is correct then it can only be said that the rhythm of daily activity must vary from place to place.

Near a stream or canal the sudden 'plop' as a water vole drops into the water is the observer's first intimation of its presence. Occasionally its course can be tracked under water, but as a rule it disappears at once, to surface some distance away or retreat into a burrow in the bank, sometimes by an underwater entrance. It may regain the bank by an upper exit. It is a steady swimmer, its rate of progress being an even $2\frac{1}{2}-3$ mph, but it is less skilful in swimming than in diving.

Bedrooms and larders

The burrows made by water voles have long winding passages with chambers for sleeping, lined with grass and hay, and chambers for storing food. The vole digs them at great speed with the forefeet, the earth being thrown out with the hindfeet. Stones are removed with the teeth and any roots that impede progress are eaten. The burrows sometimes cause considerable damage to the banks of dykes and canals. The water vole also does much good in helping to keep waterways clear of weeds and rotting vegetation.

The water vole does not hibernate, but it

has been reported to lay up considerable stores for when food is scarce. Although it is aquatic, steady rain will keep it in its burrow or cause it to gather food from near the mouth of the burrow and eat it inside. Like the water shrew (p 2570) it is sometimes found in fields far from water. It marks its home range with a scent from glands on the flanks conveyed to the ground by the hindfeet.

Vegetable eater

The water vole's diet consists mainly of succulent grasses, flags, loosestrife, sedges and other plants growing along river margins. They enjoy grain such as wheat, oats and millet, and apples are an especial favourite. It is thought that they sometimes eat freshwater snails and mussels, as well as caddis-worms and other insects, but this is not certain. Food stored in the burrow consists usually of different types of nuts, beech mast, acorns and the creeping underground stems of horsetails.

Bad weather curtails breeding

The breeding season is from early April to October. There may be fierce fighting among the males, but whether for possession of a female or for a territory is not clear. After mating, the female makes a thick-walled globular nest of reeds and grasses in a chamber under the bank, in a hollow willow, or even in a disused bird's nest. Sometimes the male helps her make the nest. After a gestation of 3–4 weeks, 2–7, usually 5, naked and blind young are born. At 10 days old their eyes are fully open and they are covered with thick, golden-red, smooth hair and at 15 days they come out into the open but do not take easily to water. By

the third week they can feed themselves, swim fearlessly and are independent of the parents. It is thought that there may be as many as 3 or 4 litters a year, as the young of early litters mature so quickly and breed before the winter. There are fewer litters if the summer is cold and wet.

The life span is little more than a year in the wild because the older individuals are driven out of their territories by the younger voles and more readily fall prey to their numerous enemies. Herons, owls, otters, stoats, weasels, rats, pike, eels and large trout all prey on the water vole.

United in battle

A predator does not always get all its own way when attacking a water vole, for sometimes a whole family will unite to do battle against it. As soon as any male member of a family is aware of an intruder approaching it 'points' with its snout upwards and stands motionless, followed by all the other males. The females in the family and the babies retreat to the water's edge. One male then engages the enemy, scuffling, squeaking and biting. If the enemy is too strong for it the water vole will run and join the females and another male takes over the fight. At each engagement the females and babies dive into the water but usually return to the bank after a short while to watch the next round. The father is usually the last to enter the battle but quite often by this time the enemy is exhausted and makes its escape.

Stephen Dalton: NHPA

class	**Mammalia**
order	**Rodentia**
family	**Cricetidae**
genus & species	*Arvicola terrestris*

△ *Water vole makes a meal of willow leaves.* ▽ *Swimming water vole leaves a wake of ripples.*

Wattlebird

The name wattlebird was originally applied to some Australian honeyeaters (p 1095) but it has since been given to a small family of New Zealand birds. Of the three species one is extinct and two are very rare but efforts are being made to preserve them. It is uncertain which are the closest relatives of the wattlebirds, but they have been linked with the Australian apostle-birds, the birds-of-paradise and the bower birds. No doubt some ancestor must have crossed to New Zealand where the three forms evolved. Wattlebirds have rounded wings, long tails, strong legs, long hindclaws and wattles, usually orange, at the corner of the mouth. The huia, an extinct wattlebird, was most unusual; male and female had bills of different shapes. Their plumage was, however, alike, being glossy black with a white band across the top of the tail.

The kokako or wattled crow is jaylike with a stout, curved bill, and is 17—18 in. long, a little smaller than the huia. The plumage is bluish-grey with a velvet-black strip in front of the eyes and above the bill. There are two subspecies; that on North Island has bright blue wattles while that on South Island has orange wattles with blue at the root. The tieke or saddleback is thrush-sized, 10 in. long, with glossy black plumage, except for a chestnut 'saddle' over the back.

The huia was known to Europeans from only the southern part of North Island. The other wattlebirds were once wide-spread in both islands but the tieke is now restricted to Hen Island in the north, the South Cape Islands in the south and a few other islands where it has been introduced in recent years in an attempt to preserve it. The kokako is still widely distributed but is rare.

▽ Claimed to be New Zealand's most versatile and beautiful singers: Kokakos or wattled crows. The South Island race **Callaeus cinerea cinerea** — the kokako with yellow and blue wattles — is now very rare, living only in the dense mountain forests and bushes. The North Island subspecies **C. c. wilsoni** is still found locally in forests. Incapable of sustained flight, it moves by rapid bounding from one leg to the other. It feeds on leaves, berries and buds, often using one foot to hold its food, the other foot for tearing.

2577

Threatened by rats

The home of the wattlebirds is the primeval forests of New Zealand. The felling of these forests is one of the main reasons for their decline and the kokako is restricted to virgin or only slightly altered forests. Introduced predators are another important factor; the tieke survives only where the rats and other mammalian predators have failed to spread. In the early 1960's, however, ship rats got ashore at the South Cape Islands. A rescue operation was mounted to save the threatened birds and 60 or so tiekes were captured and flown to other islands. In the north, tiekes have been transferred from Hen Island where it is now virtually restricted to other sanctuaries, including the Mt Bruce Reserve near Wellington.

Wattlebirds are very active but rarely fly, spending most of their time searching for food on the forest floor. Before they became rare the tiekes lived in flocks, calling harshly to each other. The kokako has no fear of man. It is one of the several species called bellbirds because of their far-carrying bell-like song.

Fruit, leaves and insect food

The food of the kokako is mainly fruit and leaves but it also eats small ground-living invertebrates which form the main part of the tieke's diet. The birds sometimes hold their food in one foot while tearing it with the bill. The tieke follows bands of other small birds, apparently to catch the insects they disturb.

Juvenile turncoats

The tieke probably mates for life; outside the breeding season it lives in flocks but each pair takes up a territory in spring. The male frequently displays to the female, bowing, singing and inflating his wattles. The wattles are larger in the male than in the female and reach their greatest size during the breeding season.

The nest is a large, loosely-woven cup of twigs, leaves and ferns, often placed in a hollow tree or rocky crevice or among dense foliage on the ground. The 2 or 3 eggs are incubated by the female for 3 weeks or more. Both parents feed the young. Young tiekes on North Island look like the adults but on South Island they have a dark brown plumage for one year. They were thought at one time to be a separate species and were called jackbirds.

The loss of the huia

When Europeans arrived in New Zealand the huia already had a restricted distribution in the mountainous regions at the south end of North Island. The Maoris snared them, luring them by imitating their calls, to obtain the tail feathers, which were prized as ornaments to be worn in the hair. Collection by the Maoris had been carried on for many years when the Europeans started to collect huias for museums. It is unlikely that either of these two kinds of collecting seriously affected their numbers, and introduced predators and forest clearance must be blamed for the disappearance of the huia, which was last recorded in 1907.

The loss of the huia is more regrettable than the loss of other recently extinct animals, because of their unusual bills. There are numerous examples in this encyclopedia of the adaptation of bills to specific feeding habits, but there is no other example of two kinds of bill within one species. The male huia had a stout, straight, chisel-like bill with which it chiselled insects and their grubs out of wood. The long, curved and rather pliable bill of the female was for probing holes and crevices in hard wood. It might be expected that this would lead to the sexes feeding apart but, in fact, they cooperated and worked together—or so it is said. On the other hand, the only firm observation on record tells of a pair of these birds in an aviary, in which the male chiselled a grub out of wood and the female then stole it from him.

class	Aves
order	**Passeriformes**
family	**Callaeidae**
genera & species	***Callaeas cinerea*** kokako ***Creadion carunculatus*** tieke ***Heteralocha acutirostris*** huia (extinct)

◁ *Not two different species of wattlebird but a male and female huia, a bird now extinct from introduced predators. The male supposedly used his stout bill for chiselling while the female used her curved bill for probing.*

Publishers: Whitcomb & Tombs, New Zealand: Macdonald U.K.

Waxbill

Waxbill

The waxbills are a group of small, colourful, reed-eating birds, that are popular cage birds. Waxbills are related to the sparrows and weavers and the waxbill subfamily includes the mannikins, munias, cordon-bleus, silvereyes and many others well known to bird fanciers. Unfortunately, several have different common names which makes the term waxbill open to confusion. The cordon-bleus, for instance, are also called blue waxbills. The waxbills proper belong to the genus *Estrilda* which also includes the striking avadavat (p 106).

Waxbills are small, usually about 4 in. long and many have finely barred upperparts. The species, known as the Waxbill, the common waxbill or sometimes the St Helena waxbill, is brown with fine barring. There is a scarlet patch around the eye, the cheeks and throat are white and in the male there is a pink tinge to the underparts. It is found in many parts of Africa and has been introduced to St Helena and Brazil. Other waxbills have a similar confusion of names. The grey or red-eared waxbill is also called the common waxbill. The upperparts are grey-brown with a pink tinge and the underparts light grey with a pink tinge turning to crimson on the belly. There is a crimson stripe through the eye and the rump is black. The grey waxbill has recently become established in Portugal from aviary escapes. One of the smallest is the 3½in. locust finch that flies in dense swarms. Its plumage is almost black with red on the face and throat. The smallest waxbill of all is the zebra or orange-breasted waxbill with a crimson streak through the eye and a crimson rump. The throat is yellow becoming scarlet underneath and the sides are barred with yellow. Waxbills live in Africa south of the Sahara apart from the avadavat in Asia and the Sydney waxbill that lives in eastern Australia.

Grain eaters

Outside the breeding season waxbills are gregarious, living in parties, sometimes of only a few birds, but others, such as the locust bird, in large flocks. The members of a party continually call to each other with shrill or soft monosyllables designed to inform each waxbill of its fellow's position and to keep the party together. Waxbills are mainly found near rivers or in swampy country where they feed on seeds, particularly those of grasses, and are particularly abundant in grassland and in crops of cereals, in association with other seedeaters such as mannikins and whydahs. In Sierra Leone the flocks are followed by rats which feed on the seeds they spill. In general, waxbills occur in too few numbers to be pests. They also eat some insects and catch flying termites.

△ The distinctive southern grey waxbill.
◁ A small and prettily coloured bird, the aptly named orange cheeked waxbill.

Husband's annexe or decoy?

The typical waxbills differ from their near relatives by building nests with tubular entrances projecting from a ball of grass that are very much like the nests of sparrows and weavers. The nest is built of grass stems or flowering heads woven into an untidy mass and fastened to vertical stems or placed on the ground among grass or herbage. Some waxbills decorate the nest with paper, damp earth, feathers and other materials and a peculiar feature of the nests of true waxbills is that there is a so-called 'cock nest' incorporated into the top or side of the nest or built a short distance away. It has been said that the cock nest is used as a roost by the member of the pair that is not incubating the eggs. There is, however, no proof of this and Derek Goodwin has suggested that the cock nests may mislead predatory birds into overlooking the real nest.

The nest is built by the female waxbill but the male helps with the decoration and with lining the nest with feathers. Both sexes incubate the 4–6 white eggs, which hatch in 2 weeks. They feed the chicks by regurgitating seeds when chicks solicit by gripping their parents' bills with their own. The young waxbills fly in 16–17 days.

Getting their own back?

Many waxbills are parasitised by some of the related whydahs, also known as widow birds. Thy whydahs lay their eggs in the waxbills' nests and their young are brought up with the young waxbills. Not all the whydahs are, however, parasites and one waxbill, the zebra waxbill, has to a certain extent reversed the situation: it lays its eggs in the nests of whydahs and bishops, but only when they have been abandoned. Bishops and whydahs finish nesting in March and the waxbills then start their nesting season taking over the nests of the bishops and whydahs and relining them.

class	Aves
order	Passeriformes
family	Ploceidae
genus & species	*Estrilda astrild* common waxbill *E. locustella* locust finch *E. melpoda* orange cheeked waxbill *E. perreini* southern grey waxbill *E. subflava* zebra waxbill *E. temporalis* Sydney waxbill *E. troglodytes* northern grey waxbill others

Waxwing

The three waxwings are named after the red tips of their secondary flight feathers which look like blobs of sealing wax. Similar but smaller blobs are also found on the tail feathers. Waxwings are starling-sized, 6—7 in. long, with prominent pointed crests, fairly long wings and slightly rounded tails. The bill is short and slightly hooked. The nearest relatives of the waxwings are the silky flycatchers of America, such as the crested phainopepla *Phainopepla nitens.*

The waxwing that breeds from northern Scandinavia to Kamchatka also breeds in western Canada and Alaska, where it is known as the Bohemian waxwing. The plumage is soft pink or grey-brown, shading to grey on the rump. There is black around the eyes and chin and the flight feathers are black with yellow and white. The black tail is tipped with yellow. The cedar waxwing of southern Canada and the northern United States is very similar but the plumage is generally paler and it lacks the yellow and white on the wings. The Japanese waxwing is like the cedar waxwing but has a red tip to the tail and red bars on the wings but no wax droplets. It lives in eastern Siberia and migrates to China and Japan.

Playing with berries

Apart from their pretty appearance waxwings are noted for their irregular migrations and wanderings. Small numbers usually migrate south in the winter but there are occasional mass movements of large numbers when waxwings can be seen in flocks which, on rare occasions, reach Central America and the Mediterranean. It has often been noticed that the waxwings in these winter flocks are sluggish, perching motionless for long periods and allowing themselves to be approached quite closely. When perching the members of a flock often huddle closely together, sometimes touching each other but usually keeping an inch or so apart. Even in winter waxwings sometimes feed each other like they do during courtship, when the food, or even an inedible object, is passed to and fro between two birds. Cedar waxwings have been seen to pass food from one to another along a line and K Parkes recounts seeing a house sparrow join the line of waxwings and swallow the berries as they reached the end.

The nomadic habits of the waxwings extend even to their breeding. Nesting takes place in the coniferous and birch forests of northern Europe, Asia and America but the waxwings shift their breeding grounds from year to year, depending partly on the local abundance of food. Perhaps related to this is the general lack of territorial behaviour. Nesting waxwings defend no territory other than the nest itself and the song is very poor, being no more than a thin trill.

▷ *Family circle. It is quite common for cedar waxwings to pass food from one to another.*

KH Himmer

2581

△ *Bohemian waxwings. The birds were probably attracted by the bright berries of the* **Cotoneaster**.

Fritz Siedel

Berry eaters

In the summer waxwings eat mainly insects, catching flies in the air or foraging on the ground. Flower petals and oozing sap are also eaten but the main food throughout the year is berries such as those of juniper, yew, rowan and elder. Blackberries, haw-thorn, holly, cherries and many other berries have also been taken.

Little aggression

Waxwings' nests are usually solitary but, as there is no defended territory, nests are sometimes placed close to each other. The nest is a cup of twigs lined with moss and grass and built in a pine or birch tree.

Even at the start of the nesting season waxwings are fairly sociable and there is only a limited amount of rivalry between the males. During courtship the feeding of the female by the male is accompanied by a display in which both birds puff out their feathers, particularly those on the rump.

The male waxwing also feeds the female while she incubates the 3–7 eggs for 2 weeks. The male also plays a small part in incubation and both parents feed the chicks.

Starvation exodus

Providing there is plenty of food many waxwings spend the winter in the northern parts of their range, even north of the Arctic Circle. Others migrate southwards and every few years there is a mass exodus known as an irruption. In winters when an irruption has taken place waxwings are seen in large flocks and stragglers appear far to the south of their usual limit of winter migration. In the winter of 1965/66 there was an irruption of waxwings from northern Scandinavia, Finland and northwest Russia and waxwings appeared as far south as Portugal, Sicily and Greece.

Irruptions of waxwings, crossbills (p 581), lemmings (p 1301) and other animals are usually caused by a season of plentiful food, when the population expands, followed by a failure of the food supply which then forces the large population to travel in search of food. The waxwing irruption of 1965/66 was predicted in advance by Kai Curry-Lindahl because these conditions had been fulfilled. The winter of 1964/65 had been unusually mild and there had been a good crop of rowan berries in northeast Europe. As a result the waxwings survived the winter well and large numbers nested in 1965. Rowans, like other plants, cannot fruit well two years running, and in the autumn of 1965 the large population of waxwings was faced with a food shortage and they were forced to move, leaving the White Sea region in late September, and arriving in southern England in mid-November with stragglers reaching Portugal and Sicily in January.

class	**Aves**
order	**Passeriformes**
family	**Bombycillidae**
genus & species	***Bombycilla cedrorum*** *cedar waxwing*
	B. garrulus *Bohemian waxwing*
	B. japonica *Japanese waxwing*

Waxwing
(Breeding grounds)
▨ Cedar (*Bombycilla cedrorum*)
▦ Bohemian (*B. garrulus*)
■ Japanese (*B. japonica*)

Weasel

Although similar in form to its near relative the stoat (p 2280), the weasel is smaller and lacks the black tip to the tail. The average length of the head and body of the adult male is $8\frac{1}{2}$ in., plus a tail of $2\frac{3}{4}$ in. The female is 1 in. or so less in total length than the male, and weighs on average 2 oz against his 4 oz. Because of this smaller size, the females are known in some districts of Britain as cane weasels and were formerly believed to represent a distinct species. The long slender body, short limbs, long neck and small head give the weasel a snake-like appearance which is heightened by its active gliding movements. The fur is a reddish brown with white on the throat and underparts, but the line of demarcation between the colours is less pronounced than in the stoat. It has been said that a weasel is small enough to pass through a wedding ring. It is hard to persuade a living weasel to perform this trick but it has been proved that a weasel's skull can be passed through a wedding ring.

The weasel is found throughout Europe, across Asia to Japan and from Siberia in the north, southwards into China and Afghanistan. Its range also extends into North Africa.

The least weasel which is widespread in North America is smaller than the Old World species as is the pygmy weasel which is said to occur in some parts of Europe. It is now fairly widely agreed that both of these should be considered as subspecies of the Old World weasel.

△ *A versatile hunter and obviously able seaman, the weasel will often swim after water voles.*

Ferocious killer

The weasel is found in almost every type of habitat including woods, scrubland, hedgerows, rocky country, barns and even at times in large towns. Although it is mainly nocturnal, it is sometimes active by day and it is possible that it has alternating spells of activity with periods of rest. It is swift and agile in movement, a good climber and swimmer and a relentless killer, hunting mainly by scent. Like other members of its family the weasel is courageous and ferocious out of all proportion to its size, and will attack animals larger than itself. It has been seen struggling to haul along a nearly full-grown rat, two or three times its own weight, killed by a bite through the base of the skull. Sometimes weasels hunt in pairs or in family parties. The normal method of hunting is to stalk or trail the prey and then to pounce swiftly and kill with a bite on the back of the victim's head. 'Charming', however, is sometimes used and this has been fully described under the red fox (p 1929).

Weasels occupy territories which they probably mark with musk from the glands under the tail. This musk is also released when an animal is severely disturbed and it may also be used to bring the males and females together in the breeding season.

Like stoats, weasels undergo a change to a white coat in autumn in the more northerly parts of their range although as a rule there is no seasonal change in their fur in more southerly parts; an occasional individual may, however, be white or partially

▽ *On the attack: a rabbit jumps into the air to escape the weasel.*

▽ *Snared: the weasel wraps itself around the rabbit for the final kill.*

white in winter. The causes of the change appear to be the same as those discussed under stoat.

The voice is a guttural hiss when alarmed and a short screaming bark when disturbed, but neither is heard very often.

Staple diet of voles and mice

The weasel's food includes rats, mice, voles, moles, frogs, small birds and their eggs and an occasional fish. It will swim in pursuit of the water vole and climb trees and bushes to rob birds' nests of eggs or young. Voles and mice are, however, the principal victims, a weasel's small size enabling it to pursue these rodents in their underground runs. When very hungry it will eat freshly killed shrews or very rarely carrion, and it does some damage in poultry runs.

Two litters in a season

The female weasel builds her nest of dry leaves, grass or moss in a hole in a bank or low down in a hollow tree. Pregnancy may occur in any month from March to August, but is most frequent in April and May. There is no delayed implantation and the gestation period is about 6 weeks. There are usually 2 litters in a season consisting of 3−8, usually 5, kittens. They are weaned at 4−5 weeks and are taught to hunt and kill by their mother. Young males of the first litter grow rapidly and are sexually mature by August, as are some of the females. Second litters grow more slowly and do not mature until their second year. A weasel has been known to live up to 6 years old.

Natural enemies

The weasel's natural enemies are the larger hawks, owls, foxes, wild and domestic cats and sometimes even stoats. The numbers taken, however, are not large and the effect on the weasel population is negligible.

Man still its enemy

In former times the hand of every game-keeper and farmer was raised against the weasel for its alleged raids on game birds and poultry. It was shot and trapped and every gamekeeper's 'gibbet' had its weasel corpses hanging on it. The accusations of poultry and game killing were undoubtedly justified to some extent but today many people have realised that the weasel does more good than harm by keeping down the numbers of small rodents in the country-side. It has been estimated that a male weasel probably kills at least 500 small rodents a year and a female 300. This, and the fact that there has been a steady decline of widespread game preserves in recent years, is reducing the number of weasels killed each year.

class	**Mammalia**
order	**Carnivora**
family	**Mustelidae**
genus & species	*Mustela nivalis* weasel *M. rixosa* least weasel

◁ *Usually an active hunter, the weasel seldom eats carrion. Here the exception is a bream.*

Weaver

Weavers are small, mainly seed-eating birds which live in Africa and Asia, but there is some confusion as to precisely which birds the term weaver refers to. Sometimes it includes the family Estrildidae which contains the avadavat, waxbills, mannikins and others, some of which have the common name of weaver. Nowadays this family is often referred to as the weaver-finches and only the members of the family Ploceidae are called weavers, or 'ploceid weavers' to avoid confusion. The Ploceidae contains the buffalo-weavers, the sparrows (p 2215), and the true weavers. The true weavers are further divided into two groups, one of which contains the bishops (p 209), the fodis (p 808) and the queleas (p 1882). This account will consider the other group alone, mainly because most of the other groups of 'ploceid weavers' have been treated separately. This is also the simplest method because the habits and appearances of this vast mass of birds are very similar, hence the confusion in classification.

There are about 70 species of weaver, most living in Africa south of the Sahara but a few live in southern Asia and the village weaver has been introduced to Haiti. They are sparrow-sized birds, about 6 in. long, and have the conical, seed-eating bills of the house sparrows. The males of many weavers have bright plumage during the breeding season but revert to the same drab, streaky plumage as the females outside the breeding season. The males of the 10 species of **Malimbus,** *sometimes known as malimbes, have red in their plumage. The red-headed weaver, or red-headed malimbe, is black all over with a red 'cap' on the crown and nape. The males of the species of* **Ploceus** *have yellow plumage. One of the best known is the village or black-headed weaver. It is golden-yellow with a black head and black streaks on the back and wings. The five Asian species of* **Ploceus** *are much alike. The baya weaver, which ranges from Pakistan and Ceylon to Sumatra, is mainly black above and pale brown underneath with yellow on the head and neck above the eye and black under it.*

Varied habitat

Weavers are found, often in large flocks, in a variety of habitats, but always where there are trees where they can roost and nest. The malimbes are found in evergreen forest while the *Ploceus* weavers are found in a variety of wooded country. The masked weaver, for instance, prefers watercourses and often nests on branches that overhang water. Others are found in dry savannahs or in marshes. As a general rule weavers in which the males are brightly coloured in the breeding season live in drier areas. The

Peter Ward

Arboreal architecture

◁ *Nests of the village weaver bird hang like pendulous fruits from the branches of a palm tree in equatorial Africa. The weavers strip so much leaf material from the palm fronds to construct their nests that eventually the palm will probably be killed.*

▷ *Yet another nest completed, the male village weaver builds nests compulsively. After each construction he 'advertises' it to the females by hanging upside down at the entrance, at the bottom of the nest, flapping his wings and chattering.*

▽ *In contrast to the rather carelessly woven nest of the village weaver is the neatly built home of the baya weaver bird. The tubular entrance, which can be as long as 2 ft, is a good deterrent against predators, coupled with the fact that the nest is suspended.*

▽▷ *The early stages. This male red-headed weaver **Anaplectes rubriceps** has a long way to go before his nest is complete. The end product will be a rough but elaborate home made of tendrils and leaf midribs. The entrance will be at the end of a downward funnel.*

KB Newman

Peter Jackson : Photo Res

Peter Johnson

dull eclipse plumage is associated with the formation of large flocks that wander about the country in the dry season to search for food. Some, like the spectacled weaver, are not so gregarious.

Grain, seeds and insect food

The majority of weavers feed on seeds, particularly grass seed, and several species have become pests of grain crops, although not to the same extent as the quelea. Insects are also eaten particularly by three species of *Ploceus*, which have slender bills, and the malimbes. These weavers hunt among the foliage or along branches and tree trunks, agilely hopping up or down like nuthatches.

Nest-building runs riot

Weavers are named after the elaborate flask-shaped nests which they make from strands of grass or palm fronds. Each nest is separate but a single large tree may contain hundreds of the nests of the village weaver. The nest is built by the male who cuts a notch in a palm frond or grass stem, then strips a 2ft thread from it, making himself a pest in palm plantations. The strips are first woven into a loop which acts as a foundation for a hollow ball, with an entrance tunnel up to 2 ft long suspended from it. When the main structure is com-

pleted the weaver displays at the entrance to attract a female. If she accepts both male and nest, mating takes place and the female lines the nest and lays her eggs. In the village weaver, the baya weaver and many others, particularly those in which the male has bright breeding plumage, the male builds several nests, courting and installing a female in each. When they run out of partners, the males continue to build nests which remain unused and usually half-finished. Some species of weaver are monogamous and the insect eaters are territorial.

The clutch consists of 2 or 3 eggs which are incubated by the female.

Belt-braces security

It must be extremely difficult for any predator to invade the nest of a weaver. The nest is not only suspended from a twig, it is protected by a vertical tunnel up to 2 ft long. One cannot, for instance, imagine a snake or a mongoose managing to climb down the outside then turn up through the entrance. Yet weavers very often employ a second line of defence by building their nests near aggressive animals that may dissuade other predators. The village weaver, for instance, often nests near human habitations or near the nests of

large birds of prey and in Malaya the baya weaver nests in trees swarming with ants.

Weaver nests are not, however, immune to cuckoos, such as the South African cuckoo *Chrysococcyx caprius*. Many cuckoos, including the European cuckoo, mimic the eggs of their hosts, choosing the right host for their eggs. Parasites of the weaver, however, have an additional problem because weaver eggs are very variable, those of the masked weaver having different patterns in different localities. Yet the South African cuckoo follows suit, and has an astonishing ability to mimic local patterns, laying eggs that match the different weaver eggs.

class	**Aves**
order	**Passeriformes**
family	**Ploceidae**
genera & species	***Malimbus rubricollis*** red-headed weaver ***Ploceus cucullatus*** village weaver ***P. ocularis*** spectacled weaver ***P. philippinus*** baya weaver ***P. velatus*** masked weaver others

▽ *Patiently waiting for their turn to feed, golden weavers* **Xanthophilus subaureus**.

DG Bone

Weddell seal

Of the four Antarctic seals—crabeater, leopard, Ross and Weddell—we know most about the Weddell seal. Unlike the others it breeds around the coastline and because it lives under the sea-ice near land it is possible to walk out over its home and to study it with comparative ease. When first discovered this seal was called Weddell's sea-leopard, after its discoverer and its spotted coat. The Weddell seal could, indeed, be mistaken for a leopard seal but for its small head and distinctly tubby body. Adult males grow to just over 9 ft and females grow a little longer, the record being 10 ft 9½ in. The colour of the coat varies, being usually dark or light grey with white streaks and spots. In summer the fur fades to a dirty brown. The seal has a dog-like face with a benign expression that is accentuated by the rolls of fat around the neck and the long, often curling whiskers.

Weddell seals are found all around the coasts of Antarctica and its neighbouring islands. The most northerly breeding colony is on South Georgia but they are sometimes seen around the Falkland Islands, New Zealand and southern Australia.

Living icebreaker

The Weddell seal is the most southerly living mammal, being found in considerable numbers along the coasts of the Weddell and Ross Seas. They are usually found in sight of land and only infrequently seen on pack ice. They spend most of their time in the water, where the temperature is usually higher than the air temperature, but on fine days in particular, Weddell seals haul themselves out of the water to bask. They prefer to lie on the ice but if this is not available they will choose the smoothest rocks they can find. They probably haul out to digest after feeding, for while they are diving their blood is diverted from the intestine to the essential organs, for example the brain.

Throughout the winter in most parts of the Weddell seal's range, and over the whole year in some parts, the sea is frozen to a depth of 4 ft or more. To breathe the seals have to either find a crack or lead in the ice or to carve a special breathing hole. These breathing holes are opened, and kept open, by vigorous sawing actions of the mouth. As a result the teeth of Weddell seals are blunted and the loss of the teeth may be a prime cause of death in old seals. It is known that Weddell seals travel long distances from one breathing hole to another but these animals are not migratory. How the seals locate their breathing holes is certainly a mystery.

△ Roly-poly female seal will lose about 300 lb in the 6—7 weeks before her pup is weaned.

Babies learn to fish

The food of Weddell seals is mainly fish, such as Antarctic cod and icefish, which they find on the sea bed and in midwater. Fish of up to 45 lb have been found in their stomachs. They also eat squid and octopus and many kinds of planktonic crustaceans. Krill are usually eaten only when the seals are hunting in the pack ice. Like other seals, young Weddell seals start by eating only crustaceans, learning to catch fish later.

Chilly reception

For most of the year Weddell seals are solitary but in early spring, from late August onwards, female seals haul out of cracks and holes in the ice to give birth to their pups. They may gather in groups of 20 or more at this time, but these concentrations are mainly the result of the seals taking advantage of the available openings in the ice. The pregnant seals do not emerge more than about 100 yd from the shore unless there is a suitable rock or islet offshore. In the northern parts of their range they sometimes give birth on land.

The single pup, which is just under 5 ft long, is born a few days after the mother has hauled out on the ice. It is born during the coldest part of the Antarctic year, yet it has no protective layer of blubber and may

suffer a drop in temperature of over 100°F as it leaves its mother's body and hits the ice.

The cow stays with her pup until it is weaned 6–7 weeks later. During this time she does not feed and changes from a plump animal hardly able to heave herself over the ice to a skinny creature whose bones are showing. She loses about 300 lb, much of which is passed to the pup as milk and converted into fat, so that by the time it is weaned the pup can hardly move. The pup may first enter the water when only a few days old. The mother is very solicitous, and even helps it out of the water. There is hardly a more charming sight than a female Weddell seal and her pup leisurely swimming underwater or floating nose to nose in the waves while the pup utters its plaintive cries.

The males have nothing to do with rearing the pup. During the pupping period they establish territories and occasionally they fight. These fights have sometimes been seen on the ice. The seals appear to be very ferocious but the tough hide and thick blubber, together with their blunt teeth, prevent much serious damage being done, although male Weddell seals are often found with one eye blinded or their flippers mutilated. Mating takes place after the pups leave the mothers. As it has never been seen it presumably takes place underwater.

Champion divers

Although Weddell seals live in an inhospitable part of the world, they are remarkably good animals to study. They are fearless of man and it is sometimes possible to place a tag on a hindflipper while the seal just looks on placidly. As they live in frozen seas one can walk out over their home and in recent years American scientists have entered the Weddell seal's home using aqualungs or underwater observation chambers. Here they recorded the strange bird-like trills and whistles that can be heard from above the ice. These calls are connected with the holding of territories but it seems that these territories are not as exclusive as those of song birds, for the dominant Weddell seal will allow other seals into the territory provided they behave respectfully.

The scientists have also studied the diving abilities of Weddell seals by attaching a depth recorder to a seal then retrieving it when the animal surfaces at the breathing hole. Weddell seals appear to be the champion divers among seals. They have been recorded as diving to 2 000 ft and as staying submerged for up to 43 minutes, 20 seconds.

class	**Mammalia**
order	**Pinnipedia**
family	**Phocidae**
genus & species	***Leptonychotes weddelli***

British Antarctic Survey

◁ *A nonchalant wave of the flipper and a benign look for the cameraman—Weddell seals are not afraid of man and are easy to approach. Scientists have been able to attach tags to a hind flipper while the seal looked placidly on.*

2591

On the move: a greater weever in active and therefore relatively harmless mood. When at rest, half buried, its dorsal fin is a constant danger.

Eyes on the top of the head and upward-tilting mouths—adaptations shown by this greater weever trio to a life in sand and gravel beds.

Weever

*There are only four species of the small weevers or weeverfishes but these are so notorious they probably have more local common names than any other fish. Their name seems to be from the Latin **vipera** for a snake. Two of their other common names are stingfish and sea dragon.*

The fish itself has a long body with a fairly small head, a wide mouth directed upwards and large eyes well up on the head. The first dorsal fin is short and supported by a few spines. The second dorsal fin and the anal fin are long and low, the tail fin is relatively large. The pelvic fins are small and lie forward of the largish pectorals. Each gill cover bears a stout poison spine. The body is greyish-brown to yellow, with spots and blotches of these colours, and the first dorsal fin is black or mainly black. The scales are arranged in oblique rows on the body. The great weever, the largest of the weevers, is $1\frac{1}{2}$ ft in length, but most weevers are only a few inches long.

Weevers range from the coasts of Norway to West Africa and also into the Mediterranean, mainly from low-water mark to 300 ft.

Hidden danger

They live on sandy bottoms, lying for much of their time buried in the sand with little more than the eyes and dorsal fin exposed. Weevers tend to be local in distribution, numerous in some places, sparse in others. Since they are often taken in nets at night they are probably more active then. In the Mediterranean the great weever is numerous and is caught for food. In other places it may be used as fish meal. The importance of weevers is the danger they present to the unwary. When lying buried they erect the dorsal fin at the slightest disturbance and the unwary bather may easily tread on one. Shrimp fishermen working inshore often take them in their nets and must be careful how they handle them. Even when they have died in the nets, the spines of the dorsal fin, which are connected to poison glands at their bases, and the poison spine on each gill cover, can cause excruciating pain. The poison is said to be sometimes fatal but reliable records of this are hard to find. The venom is a nerve poison which has distressing psychological side effects. There is reputed to have been a case of a fisherman, maddened by pain, who cut off his own finger to get rid of the poison.

Attractive eyes

The food of weevers is mainly bottom living animals, including crustaceans such as shrimps and small crabs, and small fish such as gobies, sand eels and small flatfishes. Small bivalve molluscs and marine bristleworms are also eaten. The great weever has a similar diet but feeds more especially on fishes, particularly sand eels. The weever, although apparently mainly active by night, feeds also by day, pouncing on passing prey or snapping it up as it passes close overhead. It has been suggested that its bright eyes looking up from the sandy sea bed lure fishes to it.

Spines are defensive only

The greater weever spawns from June to August: a slightly more extended season is found in the lesser weever. The eggs are $\frac{1}{25}$ in. diameter and float in the sea. They hatch in 5–10 days. The rest of their life history has not yet been studied, understandably so, perhaps, in view of the poison equipment of the fish. The dorsal spines have poison glands at their bases. The spine on the gill cover is ensheathed in skin with only its tip projecting, and there is a deep groove along both its upper and lower margins. There are no ducts to carry the poison to the spines and it is released into a wound only when the cells of the poison tissue are ruptured. This suggests that the poison is purely defensive, which is supported by observations showing that a weever does not poison its prey. A fish attacking the weever is, however, soon killed. A goby attacking a weever dies within 90 seconds, after threshing about violently and then turning on its back, but it continues to twitch for another minute after death. A blenny twice the size of a weever, attempting to swallow it, died within 2 minutes.

Human guinea pig

Another reason for supposing the poison spines of weevers are purely defensive is the black colour of the dorsal fin, which becomes very prominent when the fin is erected. Against the yellows and pale browns of the weever's skin, or against the yellow sand when the weever is buried, the effect could be like the black and yellow of a wasp's body—a warning to predators not to touch. To be an effective defence against a predator a poison need not necessarily be lethal but it must produce a painful sensation instantly, before the predator's jaws have had time to do damage. This aspect of weever biology was investigated in 1961 by Dr DB Carlisle, at the Plymouth Marine Laboratory. He held a piece of sponge—with forceps—to the poison spines of a weever, to collect the poison, then he injected small doses into his own arm. The pain was immediate and this was followed by a rise in his pulse rate and respiratory distress—even with much diluted doses. Carlisle describes the immediate pain as 'more severe than that of any other venomous sting'. The poison is due to 5-hydroxy-tryptamine, 'one of the most potent of pain-producing substances'. So rope-soled shoes for bathers can be a wise precaution.

class	**Pisces**
order	**Perciformes**
family	**Trachinidae**
genus & species	***Trachinus draco*** *greater weever* ***T. vipera*** *lesser weever* *others*

Weevil

Insects form the most numerous and diverse class in the animal kingdom, and the beetles, which include the weevils, are the largest insect group. Entomologists have already described and named about 40 000 species of weevils and every year several hundred new ones are discovered — and no doubt there are hundreds still unknown to science.

Most weevils are small, $\frac{1}{8}$ in. or so long. A few attain $\frac{1}{2}$ in. and there are tropical weevils of up to 3 in. They are generally very compact, with the head drawn out into a snout, called the rostrum. In some species the rostrum is long, slender and downward curving, and it is longest in the females; in other species it is quite short. The jaws are at the end of the rostrum. Often the antennae arise from a point halfway along the rostrum and are elbowed at the end of the first joint so that they can be folded back into a groove on each side of the rostrum. Many weevils are wingless and few of them fly much.

Trials of motherhood

All weevils are plant feeders, both as larvae and adults. The female uses her snout, with its terminal jaws, to drill a hole in a stem, bud or fruit. She then turns round and extends a long egg-laying tube or ovipositor from inside her body and deposits an egg at the end of the tunnel. Sometimes a female weevil can come to grief doing this. As she is boring into a nut or acorn her feet may slip and she is then left poised on her embedded nose, her legs waving helplessly in the air. She has no means of extricating herself from this situation and remains there until she dies. The larvae, little white legless grubs, usually live inside the plant tissues. Some pupate within their larval habitat, while others gnaw their way out and turn to pupae in the soil.

Old World weevils

The majority of weevils feed on some particular species or genus of plant, and often on a special part of the plant, and there are few plants without their associated weevils. This accounts to a great extent for the remarkable diversity of this family of beetles. The following are examples of weevils attached to particular plants.

The female nut weevil, of the Old World, bores into hazel nuts while they are still green and lays an egg in each one. The larva feeds on the growing kernel until the nut falls in the autumn, when the mature larva gnaws its way out and pupates in the soil. The proverbial 'bad nut' is a hazel nut either containing or vacated by a little white legless grub.

▽ *Glossy black weevil:* **Liparus coronatus** *a European species that feeds on carrots shows the downward-pointing head rostrum and clubbed antennae typical of weevils. This group of the Coleoptera contains more species than any other animal group: many are notorious as pests on fruit and vegetables.*

The figwort weevil is a small brown beetle with a black dorsal spot. The larvae are unusual in feeding openly on the leaves. They are covered with slime and pupate attached to the plant in cocoons formed of hardened slime. These very closely resemble the seed capsules of the figwort and no doubt derive protection thereby from insectivorous birds.

The eggs of the gorse weevil are laid in batches of a dozen or so in the seed pods of the gorse plant. The larvae feed on the seeds and pupate inside the pods, hatching on dry days in summer when the gorse seed is ripe and the pods are splitting. In this plant the pods split or dehisce suddenly with a cracking sound and the seeds are scattered quite widely. Infested pods dehisce in just the same way, but in this case it is beetles instead of the seeds that are hurled around.

So the weevils are spread as far as the gorse seeds on which they feed. This weevil has been introduced to New Zealand to control the spread of introduced gorse.

One of the largest European weevils is the large pine weevil, about ½ in. long, blackish with patches of short yellow hair. It lives on coniferous trees, especially pine, and the adult beetles do serious harm to young pines by feeding on the tender bark of the shoots and on the buds. The larvae are comparatively harmless boring into the old stumps and roots of felled trees.

Curse on cotton

The close attachment of particular weevils to particular plants has of course led to some of these beetles becoming agricultural pests. A weevil feeding on a wild plant that is brought into cultivation will almost certainly multiply enormously when its food plant, normally scattered among many other kinds of wild flowers, extends, uninterrupted, for hundreds of square miles. The pine weevil is a pest in forestry plantations of young pine, but for a weevil whose depredations are economically really impressive we must turn to the southern United States, where the cotton boll weevil costs the American cotton industry between one and two million dollars a year.

This notorious insect first invaded southern Texas from Mexico in 1892 and rapidly spread to all the cotton-growing regions. It is a typical weevil, compact, brown in colour, ¼ in. long, and it has a stout, down-curved rostrum. Its eggs are laid in the buds or, later in the season, in the fruits of the plant, one in each, and a single female may lay 100–300 eggs. The life cycle

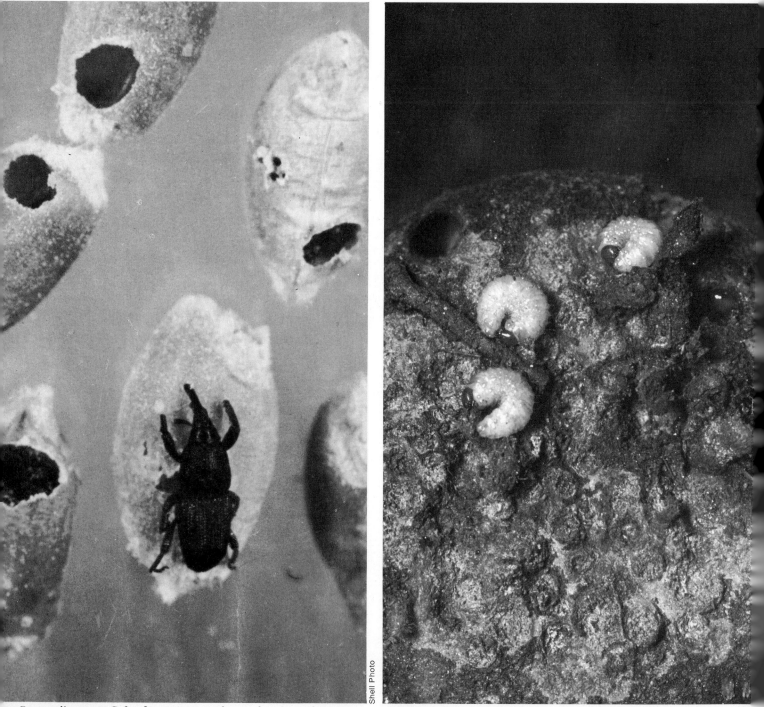

Cosmopolitan pest: **Calandra oryzae** attacks stored grain products. In a rice grain only one larva develops but a maize seed may contain several.

A cyclamen root infected with the larvae of **Otiorrhyncus sulcatus**. The larvae damage the roots of many garden plants, the adults attack foliage.

2594

takes only 3 weeks and in some localities there may be ten generations in a year. The bolls that are infested are rendered useless, and once inside the bud or fruit the larva is largely protected from sprayed or dusted pesticides. Carefully timed applications of insecticides are partly effective, and burning debris, in which the adults overwinter, is an important control measure.

From one point of view the boll weevil can be regarded as a benefactor of the southern United States. Before it invaded the area agriculture was concentrated on two crops, cotton and tobacco, and so was very vulnerable to price fluctuations. The weevil forced the farmers to diversify their agriculture and the economy of the American South has undoubtedly benefited from this. One city has acknowledged indebtedness to the boll weevil by erecting a statue to it.

Sailor's hard-tack

The Anglo-Saxon word *wifel*, from which weevil is derived, referred to the grain weevil which has infested stored grain since prehistoric times. The egg is laid, and the larva lives inside cereal grains of all kinds, hollowing them out and causing serious damage if uncontrolled. It can be destroyed by fumigation in suitably constructed stores. It also infests any foodstuffs prepared from flour, and is the weevil that we read about in the stories of sailing ship days. The staple food on board was a sort of thick, hard biscuit in which the grain weevil thrived. Fastidious sailors broke their biscuits and tapped them on the table to dislodge the little grubs and beetles; others ate them as they were and were possibly better nourished as a result.

phylum	**Arthropoda**
class	**Insecta**
order	**Coleoptera**
family	**Curculionidae**
genera & species	***Anthonomus grandis*** *cotton boll weevil* ***Apion ulicis*** *gorse weevil* ***Cionus scrophulariae*** *figwort weevil* ***Curculio nucum*** *nut weevil* ***Hylobius abietis*** *large pine weevil* ***Sitophilus granarius*** *grain weevil* *others*

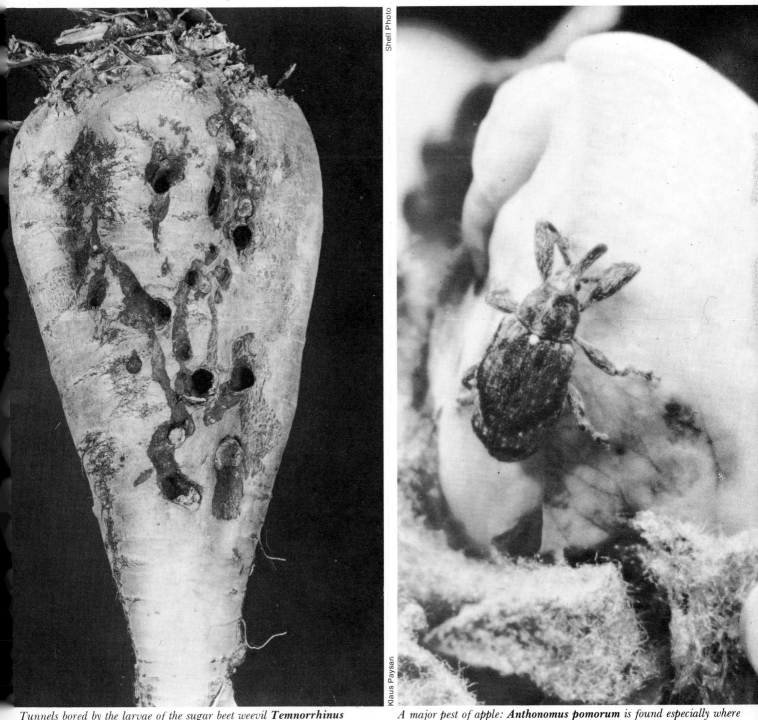

Shell Photo

Klaus Paysan

Tunnels bored by the larvae of the sugar beet weevil **Temnorrhinus mendicus** *make this vegetable useless for marketing.*

A major pest of apple: **Anthonomus pomorum** *is found especially where orchards adjoin woods, providing favourable hibernation conditions.*

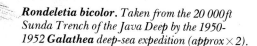

Rondeletia bicolor. Taken from the 20 000ft Sunda Trench of the Java Deep by the 1950-1952 Galathea deep-sea expedition (approx × 2).

Cetomimus indagator. Taken on the same trip, in 10 000 ft of water off the east coast of South Africa (approx × 1½).

Galathea Report

Whalefish

Whalefishes are not named for their size. They are small deep-sea fishes, the largest being 6 in. long, and most of them are 4 in. or less. They resemble the leviathans of the sea in their shape, especially in the head and relatively huge mouth, which are also similar to the head and mouth of the large whalebone whales. Whalefishes are either blind or have degenerate eyes; when eyes are present they are only about $\frac{1}{25}$ in. diameter. Like so many deep-sea fishes whalefishes are black, but in contrast with other deep-sea fishes they have brilliant patches of orange and red around the mouth and fins. The body is plump but delicate and tapers in the rear third to a relatively small tail fin. The dorsal fin is fairly large and soft-rayed and so is the anal fin that lies opposite on the underside of the tail. Both these fins have luminous patches believed to be due to a secretion from glandular patches at the bases of the fins. There are no pelvic fins and the pectoral fins are small.

The relationships of whalefishes are obscure. They were at one time placed in a separate order Cetunculi, then they were placed in a suborder near the squirrel-

fishes (p 2253). Now they are placed in the order Cetomimiformes, near the salmon-like fishes, order Salmoniformes. The 30 species of whalefishes live at depths of 6–18 000 ft in tropical seas, from the Gulf of Mexico to West Africa and in the Indian Ocean to the western Pacific.

Touch at a distance

Blind or poor sighted fishes in order to find their way about have a highly sensitive lateral line. Whalefishes have a lateral line made up of a relatively enormous hollow tube communicating with the exterior by a series of large pores, which suggests they have a highly developed distant touch and are able to detect the slightest vibrations in the water. They lack a swimbladder so the question arises as to how they maintain a position in mid-water without sinking. The answer probably lies in 'flotation appendages', typically cone-shaped, which lie between the pores of the lateral line.

Homing on vibrations

The stomach is highly distensible, so a whalefish is able to swallow fishes as large as itself. The position of the single dorsal and anal fins, set far back on the body, recalls the pikes, which capture their food by a quick dart forward. In view of what we know of the poor eyesight of whalefishes, we can only suppose they detect their prey from the vibrations the prey set up in the water. If a

whalefish then darts at its prey its lateral line organs must detect the vibrations and give accurate direction-finding as well.

Going blind with age

Practically everything that is written about the way of life of deep-sea fishes must be based on speculation, on deduction from what can be studied of the structure in a dead specimen. Nothing is known of the life histories of whalefishes, yet there is reason to suppose that the larvae live in the surface layers of the ocean. This supposition springs from a detailed examination of the eyes of two species of whalefishes. In one, *Gyronomimus*, the tiny degenerate eye is covered by a small transparent area of pigmented skin. It has no remains of a lens, no iris and no eye muscles. The retina consists of a single instead of a double layer and little is left of the optic nerve. The other, *Ditropichthys storeri*, was previously thought to have lost its eye entirely but it was realized it has an optic nerve branching out to the region where the eye would normally lie. Close examination with the microscope has since shown that there are, in the adult of this species, the remains of a retina and lens, mere vestiges, as if the eye were slowly degenerating. All things considered it seems reasonable to suggest, therefore, that the larval whalefishes have eyes and live in the surface layers where light penetrates, and that the eyes degenerate as the fish grows up and sinks down to the depths of the ocean.

Eyes and no eyes

Daylight does not penetrate to more than 3 000 ft in the sea. The human eye can detect light down to 1 500 ft, and sensitive photographic plates lowered into the sea can register faint traces of light down to 3 000 ft. Beyond this all is in absolute darkness except for flashes and sparks from luminescent animals or from animals with light organs. In depths down to 3 000 ft fishes have more or less normal eyes. Below this depth they are blind or have degenerate eyes, or else they have extra large eyes. Those with large eyes are probably the fishes that come up into the surface layers at night. At other times they use their eyes either to recognize the signals from the light-organs of members of their own species or of the species they prey upon. All fishes so far examined that live permanently in the black depths of the ocean, and have degenerate eyes, have no light-organs. The luminous patches on the fins of whalefishes are not light-organs in the strict sense, and the only other fishes with luminescent glandular secretions of this kind are the deep-sea gulper eels. Their presence in whalefishes is something of a puzzle, and so are the red and orange patches on the fins and mouths of these nearly blind fishes.

class	**Pisces**
order	**Cetomimiformes**
family	**Cetomimidae**

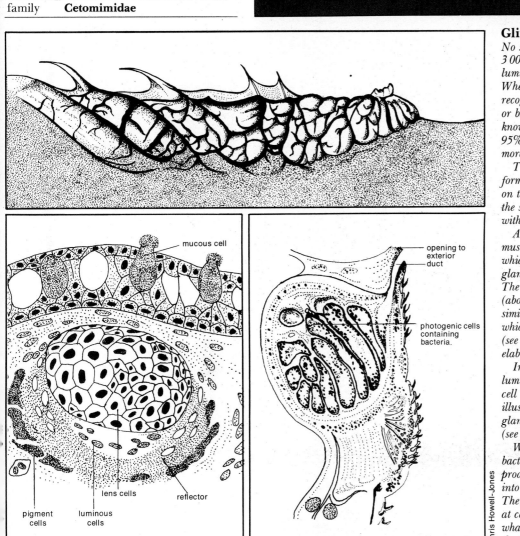

JM Bossot: Jacana

pigment cells
lens cells
luminous cells
reflector
mucous cell
opening to exterior duct
photogenic cells containing bacteria.

Chris Howell-Jones

Glimmers in the gloom

No sunlight penetrates the sea to more than 3 000 ft; only sparks and flashes from the luminous organs of fish interrupt the darkness. Whether these serve as sex- or species-recognition signals, shock predator deterrents or baits to attract smaller fishes is not known completely, but the fact remains that 95% of fishes caught from depths of 600 or more feet possess luminous organs.

There is an almost infinite variety of form, quantity and situation of these organs on the fishes' bodies, but most have them on the sides and belly—putting some whalefishes, with their dorsal glands, in the minority.

*Any classification of luminous fishes must have a primary division between those which glow directly and those which have glands containing symbiotic luminous bacteria. The spectacular viperfish **Chauliodus sloani** (above) produces its own light, through organs similar to the one illustrated at bottom left, which is from the toadfish **Porichthys notatus** (see p 2427). It is, in fact, a highly elaborated mucous gland.*

*In the other form of light production luminous bacteria are squeezed from a cell specialised to store them. This is illustrated at bottom right by the pre-anal gland of the rat-tail **Malacocephalus laevis** (see p 1191).*

*Whether or not whalefishes have symbiotic bacteria is unknown, but their light is produced by the secretion of a luminous mucus into the cavernous tissue at the fin bases. The gland of **Cetomimus gillii** is illustrated at centre: mucous from the glands of this whalefish may spread over large portions of the head and body.*

Whale shark

The largest of all sharks, yet perfectly harmless, the whale shark grows to a length of 50 ft, although large specimens of 65 ft and even 70 ft have been recorded. Exact weights are not known but it has been estimated that a 70ft whale shark would weigh about 70 tons. It is readily distinguished from any other fish by its striking colour pattern, very dark grey or brownish with white underparts, the head and body covered in white or yellow spots which are smaller and closer together on the head. The spots on the back are separated by white vertical lines. The whale shark has a long cylindrical

fins are very wide and internally they are covered within the throat by closely-set rows of sieve-like gill-rakers, each 4—5 in. long, growing out from the gill-arches. They look like miniatures of the baleen plates of the whalebone whales and have the same function of straining off plankton and small fishes. This may be one reason for their common name of whale shark.

Whale sharks are found in all the tropical waters of the world. Occasionally individuals have been reported as far north as New York and as far south as Brazil and in Australian waters.

▽ A 35ft whale shark gives a ride to small remoras clustered on the underside of its jaw.
▷ The same whale shark with an extra load.

Photos by Ben Cropp

body with longitudinal ridges along its back, one down the middle and two or three on each side. Like all sharks it has a very tough skin, that of a 60ft whale shark being 6 in. thick. The powerful tail is keeled and has an almost symmetrical fin. The head is broad and blunt and the huge terminal mouth contains hundreds of very small teeth which form a sort of rasp. The gape of the mouth is so large, 5 ft across in even a medium-sized specimen, that it is said to be wide enough to allow two men to crouch inside. The eyes are small with small spiracles placed just behind them. The pectoral fins are large and sickle-shaped and there are two dorsal fins, the second one lying above the anal fin.

An unusual feature of the whale shark, which is shared by only one other shark, the basking shark (p 158), is the presence of gill-rakers. The external gill-openings above the base of the pectoral

Docile and sluggish
The whale shark lives near the surface of the open sea, swimming sluggishly at a leisurely pace of 2—3 knots. It is very docile and one underwater photographer has described how he swam holding onto a whale shark's tail without it taking any apparent notice. It is quite harmless, the only danger from it would be from its bumping against the side of a small boat and perhaps capsizing it. Whale sharks are known to rub themselves deliberately against boats, possibly to get rid of external parasites. This has been observed by the tunny fishermen of California and Thor Heyerdahl on the *Kon-Tiki* also describes one that rubbed itself on the raft, swimming around for about an hour.

Very few whale sharks have been caught and they are not often seen except perhaps when basking at the surface. When wounded by a harpoon the shark will dive straight down or streak away at speed, dragging the boat with it. It has very great powers of endurance and does not give in easily. It

is said that if harpooned the whale shark can contract the muscles of its back to prevent the entrance of another spear. While swimming the whale shark gives out a sort of croaking sound which is possibly a form of echo-location used in navigation.

Plankton feeder
The whale shark, like the basking shark, feeds on plankton and small schooling fishes such as sardines and anchovies, by opening its huge mouth. Water rushes out over the gills leaving the fish sticking to the inner walls of the throat and to the gill-rakers. Because of this type of diet one might expect the whale shark to be lacking in teeth. Its numerous small teeth are arranged in some 310 rows in each jaw, but only about 10 or 15 rows can function at any one time. Sometimes much larger articles, such as shoes, leather belts and even large poles, are taken into the mouth.

Stewart Springer of the US Fishery Vessel *Oregon* has described seeing 30 or 40 sharks standing vertically, head up and tail down,

during a spell of calm weather in the Gulf of Mexico. They were pumping up and down in the water feeding on small fishes and accompanied by small black-fin tuna that had stirred up the sea all around with their darting and leaping. 'The whale sharks looked like black oil drums slowly rising and sinking in a long swell; only there was no swell, just a choppy sea to a hundred yards in diameter, stirred up by the tuna.'

Breeding unknown

Nothing is known of the breeding habits of the whale shark but like the basking shark it is thought to be viviparous. In a Ceylon specimen 16 eggs were found.

No economic value

The whale shark has few natural enemies. Owing to its large size only the sea's largest carnivores would attempt to attack it and a blow from its powerful tail would probably be enough to drive even the largest enemy away. It is not hunted commercially—even its liver oil does not contain vitamin A.

Gentle giant

The whale shark could truly be called a giant that does not know its own strength, and this is illustrated more specially by three incidents that took place in the last half century. In 1919 one of these sharks became wedged in a bamboo stake-trap set in water 50 ft deep in the Gulf of Siam. It appeared to have made no attempt to break its way out. In the same area, in 1950, another one was captured and beached by the local fishermen, and while details of its capture are not to hand, it would seem that the giant fish offered little or no resistance. Prince Chumbhot, reporting this incident, says it was 'towed out to deep water and released by fishermen as a matter of luck, with a piece of red rag tied round its tail'.

In 1935 a 35ft whale shark was caught almost on the doorstep of New York City, having blundered into a huge fish trap on the southern shore of Long Island. Fishermen passed ropes around the fish's tail and pectoral fins, and hoisted it aboard a lighter with the aid of a petrol engine. Dr EW Gudger described the sight of the whale shark when landed, in the following words: 'The huge body, as large as a great oak in a primeval forest, stretched back and back to a vast tail within the spread of which a tall man could stand with room to spare. The whole thing was unbelievably enormous. For the first time in my life I beheld a whale shark in the flesh, the hugest thing that I ever saw come out of the sea. I looked at it head on, I walked around it, I climbed on its broad head, and I walked down its great back. It was the most enormous, the most colossal, the most gigantic sea animal I had or have ever seen.'

class	**Selachii**
order	**Pleurotremata**
family	**Rhincodontidae**
genus & species	*Rhincodon typus*

Whelk

The name 'whelk' was originally used for one particular sea snail, the common or white whelk **Buccinum undatum** of Europe, also known as buccinum in North America where it occurs along the coast from the Arctic to New Jersey. In Scotland it is known as the buckie. The name is derived from the Latin **buccina** meaning a twisted trumpet. It was originally applied to almost any shell with a trumpet shape, and the name 'whelk' is still sometimes loosely used in this way.

The common whelk has a thick, chalky-grey to yellowish shell up to 6 in. long, and it is only one of the large family Buccinidae, which contains up to 50 genera and several hundred species. The common whelk shell has figured in many text books during the past century because of the way a sea anemone is often carried about on one. Another European species is the red whelk, or almond whelk, **Neptunea antiqua.** Its shell is usually 4½ in. long but it may be as much as 8 in. There is a red whelk **Charonia rubicunda**, unrelated to true whelks, that lives in Australian seas.

One of the best known American whelks is the channelled whelk **Busycon canaliculatum** found from Cape Cod to Florida. Its shell is 5 – 7½ in. long. Related to the Buccinidae, but forming a separate family, Nassariidae, are the dog-whelks or mud snails, often attracted to lobster pots in the course of their scavenging. These dog-whelks are distinct from the European dog-whelk, **Nucella lapillus,** which belongs to the family Muricidae. Its shell, which is 1 – 1½ in. long, may be yellow, white, mauve or brown, and is often banded. The members of the family Muricidae bore holes through the shells of other molluscs then insert their long proboscises and eat the flesh, or else they prise open bivalve shells using a special tooth on the lip of their own shell aperture. The American whelk-tingle, rough whelk or oyster drill **Urosalpinx cinerea,** is another of the same family and a serious pest of oysters. It was introduced into British waters with American oysters about 50 years ago. Whelks of this family yield a dye that was once highly valued: the Tyrian purple. Among other 'whelks' are the heavy whelks of the Vasidae family of Australia and the distantly related needle whelks belonging to the family Cerithiidae.

Cannot live on the shore

The common whelk is found on every kind of sea bottom from near low water to great depths and its abundance has in the past made it important as food. Though large empty shells are familiar objects on the shore, the larger living individuals normally live offshore and it is only the small ones

◁ A common or white whelk searches for food with its long siphon, which may be extended for 2 in., or even twice the length of its shell.

▽ Top: Periscopic feeding. All that can be seen of netted dog whelks **Nassarius reticulatus** is their siphons protruding through the sand, now used for breeding. At the tip of each is the mouth with its rasping radula. Bottom: A dead common whelk is placed on the sand and within minutes the whelks surge forward to feed.

▷ Top: A rusted bucketful of marine life. A mass of common whelk's spawn, sea squirts, contracted sea anemones and sponges.

▷ Bottom: An assortment of European dog whelks. Their shells are 1 – 1½ in. long, all varying greatly in colour and often with bands.

that occur between tide marks, usually in well-sheltered places where there is mud between large stones. The common whelk is not suited to life on shore. When uncovered by the tide it may cling to a rock until the tide returns, but on mud or sand, instead of retreating into its shell and using the operculum to seal the aperture as would a winkle, it continues to crawl about. Thus the water drains from the gill cavity and the tissues gradually dry out. In the Bay of Fundy, on the east coast of Canada, where the tidal range is the greatest in the world, many of these whelks are left exposed on the shore during the great ebb of the spring tides and so die.

Long probing feeding-tube

The common whelk feeds by means of a long proboscis which may be extended for about 2 in. or even twice the length of the shell. At its tip is the mouth with its rasping, file-like radula. The whelk's food consists of fresh carrion, crabs, worms and bivalve molluscs which it finds with a long siphon which sways about sampling the taste of the water. The siphon also brings clean water into the gill cavity while the whelk is buried or feeding on rotten flesh. Plaice caught in nets are sometimes attacked by whelks; the proboscis is inserted directly into the flesh of the fish, and 10—20 whelks may 'gang up' on a single fish. Whelks also insert the outer lips of their shells into the valves of cockles, scallops, mussels and oysters, thus preventing them from closing and allowing the proboscises to rasp away inside. The American *Busycon* also feeds on bivalves, but if the valves cannot be wedged apart this whelk chips away at their edges with its own shell until the proboscis can enter.

Young whelks feed on eggs

As familiar as whelks themselves, are the masses of usually empty egg cases that are so often cast ashore. Sometimes called 'sea wash balls', they are said to have been used by sailors as sponges, which they closely resemble. Before their real nature was realized, they were named by John Ellis as a species of coralline *Alcyonium*. The female whelk lays her eggs between October and May, turning herself around as she deposits them in a mass of capsules. Though the lower egg cases in the mass are usually fastened to some hard object, the mass often breaks free and many empty egg cases are eventually washed up on the shore. A single female produces up to 2 000 capsules, each about 1 in. across and joined to its neighbour by projections around the edge. However, several females may together produce a mass over 1 ft across made up of as many as 15 000 capsules. Smaller capsules are usually produced by smaller whelks. Each egg capsule contains several hundred eggs, occasionally more than 3 000, each about $\frac{1}{80}$ in. across; from these only 10—30 young snails emerge. The reason for this is that the remaining eggs, though fertilised, serve to nourish those few embryos that are destined to become small whelks. They are known as nurse cells or food eggs. The snails that finally emerge after about two months are about $\frac{1}{8}$ in. long. However, some of the unhealthy, developing young may be devoured by their healthier companions before hatching.

Easy to catch

The whelk's habit of eating dead or dying animals has been exploited by fishermen as a means of catching whelks for food or for bait. They have been considered delicacies at least since the days of Ancient Rome. Whelk 'pots', made of withy and twine on an iron frame, are lowered to the sea floor with freshly dead crab or fish inside. Another method of catching whelks is to tie the crabs or fish in a bunch and lower this into shallow water just offshore. Whelks are attracted to the carrion from a considerable distance. Whelks themselves are preyed upon by bottom-feeding fish, such as rays and dogfishes, and a single cod may have 30—40 whelks in its stomach at one time. Some idea of how numerous they are can be seen by the record of over 10 tons being caught in one small area in 7 months.

DP Wilson

DP Wilson

phylum	**Mollusca**
class	**Gastropoda**
subclass	**Prosobranchia**
order	**Stenoglossa**
family	**Buccinidae**

Popperfoto

A green lizard provides a substantial meal for a dark green whip snake—a large yet agile hunter.

Whip snake

The whip snakes are, as their name suggests, extremely slender with long tapering tails. The name has been applied to very close relatives of the racers (p 1896) of North America and Eurasia, to other snakes of the family Colubridae that live in the Orient and to Australian members of the family Elapidae. The name is most commonly used for the European or dark green whip snake and its relatives. They are found mainly around the Mediterranean from the Atlantic coast of France to the Persian Gulf and through North Africa. One species can be found as far north as Poland.

The dark green whip snake is the largest European snake, growing to over 6 ft and occasionally up to 8 ft, one third of this length being tail. The head is fairly prominent and the eyes are large. The colour is, typically, yellowish-brown or pale olive with black bars and spots at the front end and yellowish-white underparts. One of the commonest snakes around the Adriatic, it ranges from southern France and northern Spain through Switzerland and Italy to Asia Minor. Close relatives of the dark green whip snake are Dahl's whip snake and the brown whip snake, both ranging from the Balkans into western Asia.

Of the Oriental whip snakes, the pencil-slim common green whip snake may grow to 6 ft or more but is usually 3 – 4 ft. The tail is long, the eyes large with horizontal pupils and the snout is long and pointed. The body is bright green, but the green is made up of minute spots of yellow on a blue background. It lives in India and Southeast Asia. The brown speckled whip snake is very similar in appearance except that it is brown. It lives in southern India and Ceylon.

The Australian whip snakes belong to the family Elapidae and are venomous. The yellow-faced whip snake of all states except Tasmania may be 3 – 4 ft long and its bite has an effect similar to that of a bad wasp sting. The black whip snake grows to 6 ft or more and has a more severe, sometimes dangerous, bite.

Difficult to capture

The common characteristic of the three kinds of whip snake, apart from their slender bodies, is their ability to move fast, although this may be more apparent than real, as in the racers (p 1896). They can, however, disappear into undergrowth or under stones with remarkable speed and are very difficult to capture. The French authority on snakes, Lataste, tells how he saw a certain whip snake at a particular spot many times over a period of two years but was never able to catch it.

The whip snakes of the Mediterranean region usually live on the ground in dry places among shrubs and stones, although they sometimes climb among bushes. The Oriental whip snakes, however, spend most of their time in trees and are sometimes called tree snakes. Because of their colour and shape they are easily mistaken for hanging vines or twigs. The Australian whip snakes live on the ground in dry areas.

Good vision

Whip snakes feed mainly on small reptiles especially skinks and other lizards which they chase and swallow alive, instead of enveloping them in their coils. Voles, mice and large insects such as locusts are also eaten. Tree-living whip snakes take large numbers of tree frogs and also catch birds up to the size of a dove. The horseshoe whip snake enters houses in Spain and Algeria where it preys on mice and robs the nests of sparrows.

The Oriental whip snakes are unusual in having horizontal pupils that appear as long slits. There is also a groove running along the snout to each eye which probably allows each eye to see objects in front of the head and allows stereoscopic vision, as the eyes' field of vision overlaps. The Oriental whip snakes are among the few snakes which can detect motionless prey.

Eggs or live young

Mediterranean whip snakes lay their eggs in holes or crevices in the ground or under stones. The eggs vary in number from 3 in the horseshoe whip snake to about 15 in the dark green whip snake. The Australian whip snakes also lay eggs, varying from 3 to 6 in number, but the Oriental whip snakes give birth to 3 – 22 live young.

St Paul's viper

Most descriptions of Mediterranean and Oriental whip snakes emphasise their ferocity. At one time the Mediterranean species had the generic name of *Zamenis*, alluding to its aggressiveness, while the green whip snake of India and Ceylon is popularly believed to strike at the eyes and in Singhalese is called the 'eye plucker'. The name is well earned for, although whip snakes do not necessarily aim at the eyes, they strike aggressively with the mouth open, even attempting to strike through the window of a cage. They inflict painful bites, but no venom is injected although the saliva of the green whip snake can cause a local swelling. It has been suggested that the dark green whip snake, which is common on many of the Mediterranean islands from Corsica and Sardinia eastwards, was the 'viper' that bit and clung to St Paul's hand after he had been shipwrecked on Malta. According to the story in the Acts of the Apostles the Maltese were surprised that St Paul came to no harm and 'said that he was a god'. One might expect that the local people would know which animals were dangerous but in several parts of the world snakes, geckos and various insects are supposed to be deadly when they are in fact harmless.

class	Reptilia
order	Squamata
suborder	Serpentes
family	Colubridae
genera & species	*Coluber hippocrepis* horseshoe whip snake
	C. jugularis brown whip snake
	C. najadum Dahl's whip snake
	C. viridiflavus dark green whip snake
	Ahaetulla mycterizans green whip snake
	A. pulverulentus brown speckled whip snake
family	Elapidae
genus & species	*Demansia olivacea* black whip snake
	D. psammophis yellow-faced whip snake, others

Whirligig beetle

The small beetles that gyrate rapidly on the surface of the water on ponds and canals are called whirligig beetles. The name dates from the 15th century and originally a whirligig was a toy that spun. Most of them belong to the genus **Gyrinus** and are shiny blue-black or dark bronze in colour. They swim with the second and third pairs of legs only. These legs have their segments flattened and fringed with hairs, making them effective oars. The first pair of legs are slender and quite normal, and they take little or no part in swimming. The antennae are short and clubbed and the eyes are remarkable in being divided into separate upper and lower compound eyes on each side of the head. Whirligig beetles have wings and fly readily and will quickly escape from an open aquarium.

Ten species of **Gyrinus**, all very similar in appearance, are found in Europe and some species of whirligig beetle are almost cosmopolitan. In one member of another genus, **Orectochilus**, the upper surface, instead of being shiny, is clothed with thick yellowish-grey hair. It is known as the hairy whirligig and lives in running water, gyrating on the surface only at night. By day it hides under the bank. It is the only species of its genus found in Europe: one other kind of hairy whirligig is known from Africa and a number from Asia. The Gyrinidae is a relatively small beetle family, containing a total of about 400 species, as compared, for example, with the 40 000 species of weevils.

Surface swimmers—whirligigs **Gyrinus natator**.

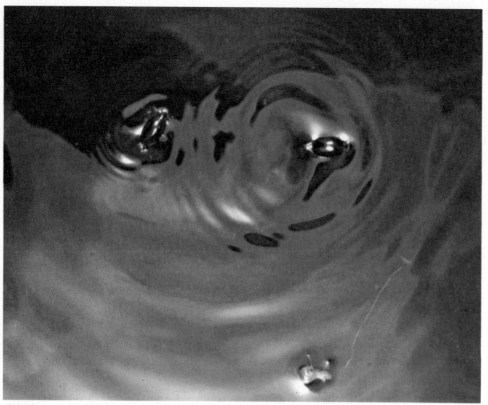

F Greenaway: NHPA

Ripples on a pond: **Gyrinus natator** *whirl around on their specially flattened mid- and hind-legs.*

They must keep a constant pattern of objects on the bank in view. The fact that they can do this while weaving about in elaborate convolutions implies a remarkable degree of co-ordination of movement and vision.

Whirligigs can swim well under water and dive readily when alarmed. They always carry a bubble of air attached to the hind end; this bubble is probably used for respiration when the beetles rest clinging to underwater plants.

They make no attempt to hide themselves at any time and seem to be an easy prey for birds and fishes, for all their active movement. They are probably protected by their power to exude a milky fluid when molested. This is variously described as smelling 'disagreeable', or, in one American whirligig, *Dineutes americanus*, 'like apples', but it is likely to function as a repellent in all cases.

So far as is known whirligigs feed on small insects that fall onto the water surface, which they seize with their long, mobile front legs.

Aquatic larvae

Whirligigs over-winter as adults and the females lay their eggs in spring, end to end in rows on submerged water plants. The larvae hatch and grow rapidly. They swim in a wriggling manner or creep about the bottom feeding on other insects and to some extent on vegetable matter. Their pointed jaws are hollow for sucking the juices of their prey. When fully grown the larva is very slender and over $\frac{1}{2}$ in. long. The joints between the segments are deeply indented and there is a row of feathery gills along each side of the body, one pair on each abdominal segment except the last, which has two pairs. The last segment also has two pairs of hooks which are said to be used for climbing about on water plants. About the end of July the larvae climb up the stems of emergent water plants and spin cocoons above the surface. The adults appear a month or so later and it is at this time, in late summer, that whirligigs are extremely abundant.

The larva of the hairy whirligig is found among gravel in shallow flowing water, and keeps out of sight, like the adult.

Semi-submerged skaters

Their capacity for scooting about like tiny speed boats, weaving around in dense crowds but never colliding, is the whirligigs' most characteristic feature. They do not float on the surface film like pond skaters. The undersurface and legs are wettable and are immersed in the water but the shiny or hairy upper surface repels the water and remains dry. The antennae are held actually in the surface film and are believed to be sensitive to changes in its curvature, thus enabling the beetles to avoid collision with each other. Each beetle makes a dimple in the film around it and throws up little bow waves in front. The two pairs of swimming legs do not rely only on their fringe of hairs for propulsion, as do those of most other water insects. The flattened joints fold up like a fan on the forward movement and then open up for the backward propulsive stroke.

Maintaining position

A group of whirligigs can be seen to maintain its position on a pond, or even in slowly flowing water, without simply scattering, as would perhaps be expected from the maze-like movements of the individuals. The two separate pairs of eyes are so positioned that one is under the water and the other above, and there is little doubt that their facets or ommatidia are adapted respectively for aquatic and aerial vision. There seems to be only one possible means by which the beetles can maintain their position when swimming.

The best of both worlds: divided compound eyes allow a whirligig to see both above and below water.

Anthony Bannister: NHPA

Aquatic all-rounder

A whirligig beetle is unusual in enjoying the best of three worlds. Although it spends much of its time sculling about on the surface it can easily take off and fly, skimming over the surface to look for a fresh feeding ground. Then it noses over into a steep dive, using its wing cases as a parachute, and lands gently on the water. It can then, if necessary, shut its wing-cases, trapping a bubble of air under them, and submerge like a submarine or, better still, a skin-diver.

phylum	**Arthropoda**
class	**Insecta**
order	**Coleoptera**
family	**Gyrinidae**
genera & species	**Gyrinus natator** *whirligig* **G. marinus** *whirligig* **Orectochilus villosus** *hairy whirligig, others*

Whistler

The whistlers, or thickheads, are small birds with melodious, often whistling songs. They are related to the flycatchers. They are found in Australia, New Guinea, Malaysia, the Philippines and islands of the South Pacific. In Australia some whistlers have alternative names such as robin, shrike-thrush or tit-shrike. As the alternative names suggest they have large heads and rather shrike-like bills. Some have crests and a few have wattles or bare patches of skin. They vary in size from 6 to 13 in. The plumage usually contains yellow or green and black and the throat is usually white.

The golden whistler, like most other whistlers, is sexually dimorphic, the male having a bright plumage that contrasts with the dull female. The male has a white throat which is separated from the yellow breast and abdomen by a narrow black band that joins the black on the head. The back is bright olive green, the wing tips and tail grey and black. The female has no yellow plumage and is grey except for buff on the breast. The golden whistler is found from Malaya to Australia and in the Fiji Islands. Another Australian whistler is the rufous whistler, the male being chestnut where the golden whistler is yellow. The black band across the chest continues along each side of the throat to the bill. The female, in contrast, is streaked with white on the abdomen.

Birds of ground cover

Whistlers are found mainly in forest and scrub; the golden whistler is found in the open green forests and in wattle scrub but the white-breasted whistler of Australia is found in the mangrove swamps of the northern coast. In general, they are found where there is good cover and they spend their time on or near the ground. Outside the breeding season they gather in flocks, often with other birds. They are usually shy birds and their habits are not known in detail but the golden whistler often goes into suburban gardens and may become quite tame.

Mainly insect eaters

Most whistlers feed on insects, such as beetles and grasshoppers, which they glean among foliage or on the ground. The whistling shrike-thrush peels bark with its bill to disclose insects and their larvae underneath. A few whistlers eat berries and some of these lack the rictal bristles around the base of the bill which are generally an adaptation for sweeping up insects and are probably a disadvantage in berry eating.

Wistful songs

The songs of the whistlers are among the finest of any Australian bird and early European settlers called the golden and rufous whistlers 'thunderbirds' because they were stimulated to sing by loud noises. The rufous whistler sometimes sings to defend

Almost-fledged rufous whistler awaits a meal from its mother. The male, too, helps feed the chicks.

its territory all the year round. It has a number of phrases in its song including sounds like a whip-crack. Other whistlers, such as the olive whistler, have strangely wistful calls. The golden whistler sounds like a man calling a dog, the notes usually being represented as 'wi-wi-wi-wi-*wit*'. Male whistlers defend their territories by singing and performing bowing displays and the female rufous whistler assists in the defence. In this species both sexes sing during courtship, the female answering the male's whip-crack calls.

The cup or saucer shaped nest is constructed of dead leaves and dry grass and is lined with feathers or fibres. It is placed in a fork of a tree, usually in an upright rather than a horizontal fork. There are 2–4 white or brownish eggs which are incubated by both parents or by the female alone for about 15 days. Both parents care for the young which stay in the nest for about a fortnight. They sometimes perform distraction displays to lure away predators.

Record varieties

There are about 80 subspecies of golden whistler—a record among birds. The reason for this is probably that its range from Malaysia to the Fijis includes a vast number of islands, including the Indonesian archipelago and the Solomon Islands. In the latter group there is a separate subspecies on each major island. On Malaita, for instance, the male lacks the black band across the breast, on Rendova the wings are black rather than olive and on Rennell Island the male is drab and indistinguishable from the female.

Here, it seems, we have another example of birds evolving in isolation, but at the subspecies level instead of between species as in Darwin's finches. As far as is known, there seems to be no adaptive function in plumage changes as there is in the bill shapes of Darwin's finches. The subspecies of golden whistlers appear to have just evolved in isolation, but if they met they probably would not interbreed; other females, for instance, would not recognize the Rennell Island male as a possible mate.

class	**Aves**
order	**Passeriformes**
family	**Muscicapidae**
genera & species	***Colluricincla rectirostris*** *whistling shrike-thrush* ***Pachycephala olivacea*** *olive whistler* ***P. pectoralis*** *golden whistler* ***P. rufiventris*** *rufous whistler* *others*

White butterflies

The term 'white butterflies' is sometimes used to cover the whole of the great butterfly family Pieridae, but many pierids, especially tropical species, are brilliantly coloured yellow, orange and red, so this usage is rather misleading. The European white butterflies comprise the members of the subfamily Pierinae, exclusive of the 'orange-tips' and those of the Dismorphiinae, one of which is the wood white. The pierine whites are the familiar cabbage white butterflies. In the New World one species, accidentally introduced from Europe, is a serious pest of cultivated plants of the cabbage family. This is *Pieris rapae,* the small white or (in America) the European cabbage butterfly. There are also a number of indigenous American species of **Pieris**. Another North American pierine is the pine white, the larva of which feeds on pine, an unusual diet for a member of this family of butterflies. It is sometimes abundant enough to do considerable damage in pine woods and plantations. Some species of whites range up to 18 000 feet or more, the highest habitat known for any butterflies. These include species of **Phulia** and **Piercolias** in the Andes and **Baltia** of central Asia.

The whites, and all other members of the Pieridae, pupate like the swallowtails. The pupa is attached by the tail, usually to a vertical surface, and has an anchoring girdle of silk surrounding it at midbody. It is thus suspended rather like telephone linesman at work. The eggs are bottle-shaped and ribbed and stand upright on the leaves when laid. The larvae are often elongate and green but show considerable diversity of form.

▽ *Marbled mating of a pair of meadow whites* **Pontia helice***. Close relatives of the Bath white, they live throughout South Africa.*

Crop pests

The large white and the small white are notorious pests of cabbage and other brassica crops, on which their larvae feed. The large white is generally less numerous but it sometimes migrates in huge swarms, which occasionally cross the Channel to southern England. Its bristly larva is dull green and yellow with blackish mottling. It has an unpleasant smell and is distasteful to birds, although they eagerly search for and eat the pupae during the winter. The larva is heavily parasitised by the small ichneumon wasp *Apanteles glomeratus*. It is often found feeding on 'nasturtium' *Tropolaeum* as well as on cabbage.

The very abundant small white also migrates in swarms, but less frequently. Its larva is not protected by any distasteful properties, but is well camouflaged by its green colour. It also suffers heavily from parasites. In both species the sexes are distinct, the black markings of the females being heavier and always including a pair of black spots on the forewing. Both have a spring and a summer brood, of which the latter is more strongly marked with black in both sexes.

The small white has spread widely over the world, probably by accidental conveyance of pupae. It reached Quebec about 1860 and in the next 25 years spread all over temperate North America. It appeared in New Zealand in 1929 and in southern Australia some years later, reaching Tasmania about 1940. In these regions biological control has met with some success. The agent used is a chalcid wasp (p 408) *Pteromalus puparum* which lays its eggs in the newly formed pupa.

Harmless white butterflies

The third common European white butterfly, the green-veined white, is similar in size and appearance to the small white, but differs in having the veins of the wings bordered with greenish-grey scales on the underside. The sexes and the spring and summer generations differ in much the same ways as the large and small whites. The larva feeds on various wild Cruciferae, such as hedge mustard and cuckoo flower, and does not attack cultivated crops. This is one of the butterflies in which a distinct race or subspecies has evolved in Ireland. It is more strongly marked than even second brood butterflies from Great Britain. The black-veined white has no distinct markings except an outlining in black of the wing veins. It is common in continental Europe and was widely spread in southern England during the last century. By 1900 it had become confined to Kent and it became extinct in the 1920's. Recent attempts to re-establish it have not succeeded, and it seems most probable that a climatic change, away from hot summers and severe winters, led to its dying out in Britain. The larva feeds on sloe, hawthorn and plum, hibernating through the winter in a communal web.

Historic butterflies

The Bath white is distinctively marked, having areas of both wings dappled with greenish-black. Its English name is a piece of whimsy derived from the circumstance that at some time during the 18th century

Klaus Paysan

SG Giacomelli

△ Small white butterflies congregate around a patch of mud to drink.

◁ Pupae of the large white overwinter on a tree trunk. The pupal stage involves a great amount of internal rearrangement from the caterpillar to the adult butterfly.
Metamorphosis of insects into different forms is controlled by hormones produced in the brain—the pupa develops when the epidermal cells are exposed to a relatively large amount of moulting hormone and a small amount of juvenile hormone. The adult butterfly develops when no more juvenile hormone is produced. To complicate matters the whole sequence of events is genetically controlled. The pupa, common to many insects, represents a protective transitional stage, and must have had selective value in the course of evolution.

a young lady of Bath executed a piece of needlework in which the butterfly was depicted. It is also interesting to note that a specimen of it, collected and preserved in 1702, shortly after Queen Anne came to the English throne, is preserved in the Hope Department of Entomology at Oxford. It is common in continental Europe but a rare summer visitor to Britain.

The wood white and two other related species are remarkable in being the only Old World representatives of the subfamily Dismorphiinae, which is otherwise entirely confined to South and Central America. In that region about 100 species are known, many of them brightly patterned.

Butterfly pigments

In many of the most brilliant butterflies the colours are produced by the effect known as 'structural coloration' (p 1508). In the Pieridae, of which the 'whites' are a sober coloured minority, we find bright colours, red, orange and yellow as well as white, which are due to chemical pigments produced by the insect and deposited in the scales of its wings during development. These pigments are known as pterines; the white substance in the scales of the common white butterflies is a particular pterine called leucopterine, which chemically resembles uric acid and was formerly confused with it. The marbled white butterfly has wings checkered with white and black, but is a relative of the meadow brown (p 1445) not of the true whites. If a preserved specimen of a pierid, say a large white, and one of a marbled white are exposed together to ammonia vapour the large white will remain unchanged but the colour of the marbled white will deepen to a yellow tint. This is because its white pigment is of a wholly different nature; it is a flavone or anthoxanthin, a type of pigment derived from the food plant. The fact that the scales of the wood white also contain flavone pigment does not mean that it is related to the marbled white, but it does underline its quite remote relationship with the other more typical pierid butterflies.

phylum	**Arthropoda**
class	**Insecta**
order	**Lepidoptera**
family	**Pieridae**
genera & species	***Aporia crataegi*** *black-veined white* ***Leptidea sinapis*** *wood white* ***Melanargia galathea*** *marbled white* ***Neophasia menapia*** *pine white* ***Pieris brassicae*** *large white* ***P. napi*** *green-veined white* ***P. rapae*** *small white* ***Pontia daplidice*** *Bath white* *others*

◁ △ *Large white—close up: the coiled proboscis is formed by the highly modified maxillae held together by interlocking spines.*
◁ *A colourful white—the purple tip* **Colotis danae,** *a butterfly of the low African veld.*

White-eye

The white-eyes, also known as silver-eyes, particularly in Australia, are small birds, about 4–5 in. long, that are found in most of the Old World tropics from West Africa to the Pacific Islands, and from Japan in the north to Macquarie Island in the south. Within this vast range they show a wide variation in plumage, particularly among the species living on islands. White-eyes are also popular cagebirds. Several of the pochard group of ducks are also called white-eyes.

Most of the 85-odd species of white-eye are classed in the genus **Zosterops**, which is sometimes used as a common name for white-eyes. The bill is usually slender and curved, the wings rounded and the tail square. As their name suggests a principal feature is the white ring of minute feathers around the eye. In some African species the ring becomes a large patch and in others it is missing. The yellow-spectacled white-eye of the Lesser Sunda Islands has a yellow eye ring. Both sexes of white-eyes are similar, and are usually green or yellowish above and grey or yellow below. Those living on islands often lack yellow in the plumage.

Among the best-known of the white-eyes is **Zosterops senegalensis** that ranges from Senegal to South Africa. It exists in several different forms and is known as the green or the yellow white-eye depending on the brilliance of its plumage. The common eastern white-eye, known as the coast white-eye in Malaya, ranges from Afghanistan to Indonesia. It is greenish yellow above and yellow and grey underneath with a black tail. The commonest Australian white-eye is the western silver-eye, or greenie, often a pest in orchards and suburban gardens. It is olive-green above, grey underneath.

Variation with climate

White-eyes have a very wide range of habitats. They live in flocks of up to 100 in wooded country, ranging from dense forests, where they are found only on the borders, to scrub. They are found in the Australian coastal mangrove swamps and in the wooded highlands up to the tree line.

Often a species is confined to a single type of habitat; one finds different white-eyes living close together but not overlapping as one travels up a mountain side or from dry to wet forest. RE Moreau has shown that the white-eyes in Africa vary from one environment to another in accordance with several biological rules. Bergmann's rule, for instance, states that the body-size of an animal becomes larger towards the cooler part of its range, an adaptation to the conservation of heat. This happens in the African white-eyes. Their wing-lengths also increase with altitude and their plumage gets darker in areas of increasing humidity.

Flocks of white-eyes keep in touch with

quiet calls as they forage among bushes and trees in a straggling procession. As one flies from a tree, calling, others follow in a stream. Most do not migrate but the grey-backed white-eyes of Tasmania migrate across the Bass Strait to New South Wales.

Pests of soft fruit

White-eyes eat insects, fruit and nectar. The insects are found among the trees and include aphids, caterpillars and flying termites. Like the honeyeaters (p 1095), white-eyes have tongues that have brushes at their tips which are used for mopping up nectar or fruit pulp. The common white-eye of the Orient, for instance, pierces the base of hibiscus and other flowers with its pointed bill then licks out the nectar with its tongue. Soft fruit such as paw-paw, figs and grapes are treated in much the same way, by piercing the skin and extracting the juice and pulp. Thus the damage to a crop is out of all proportion to the amount they actually eat as they remove only a small part of each fruit. The flocking habits of white-eyes increase the amount of the damage and there is an Australian record of 1 200 white-eyes being shot in one orchard in one day.

A family similarity

For all their variety in plumage white-eyes have very similar nesting habits. At the beginning of the breeding season the flocks split up and the males sing a pleasant, far-carrying trill. The nest is a deep cup, about 2 in. across, slung between two twigs. It is made of lichen or grasses, bound with cobweb and lined with finer grasses, kapok or sheep's wool. Both parents incubate the 2 or 3 eggs for 10–12 days. The chicks stay in the nest for 9–13 days and are fed on caterpillars, pulped by passage through the parents' bills. After they have fledged, the chicks stay with their parents for an- .... .. weeks.

△ *Fig eater: the Cape white-eye* **Zosterops virens** *pierces the skin of fruit with its sharp beak to extract pulp with its brush-like tongue.*

Successful colonists

The white-eyes have been extremely successful at colonising islands. They were introduced to one place in the Hawaiian Islands and have since spread around the islands by themselves. About 1856 Tasmanian grey-backed white-eyes arrived in large numbers on the west coast of North Island, New Zealand. From there they rapidly colonised the whole of New Zealand. It is very unlikely that these white-eyes were assisted by a ship-borne passage because they arrived in such large numbers. This journey was 1 200 miles long, but perhaps more astonishing is their colonisation of the sub-Antarctic island of Macquarie about 700 miles south of New Zealand.

The white-eyes' success in colonisation probably lies in their gregarious habits. By travelling in flocks there is a good chance of sufficient numbers arriving, even though many die on the way, and then by keeping together they form the basis of a colony.

class	**Aves**
order	**Passeriformes**
family	**Zosteropidae**
genus & species	***Zosterops australasiae*** *western silver-eye* ***Z. lateralis*** *grey-backed white-eye* ***Z. palpebrosa*** *coast white-eye* ***Z. senegalensis*** *yellow or green white-eye* ***Z. wallacei*** *yellow-spectacled white-eye* *others*

The stalks of the eggs actually pierce the outer layer of cells of a leaf and, as they are hollow, they draw moisture from the leaf by capillary action. So long as the plant is well supplied with water, development of the eggs proceeds normally. If the leaf withers, however, the development of the egg is arrested; and if the plant wilts during a drought the egg goes into a resting stage until more sap is available. Sometimes whitefly eggs go into a resting stage for no obvious reason. All these are almost certainly adaptations to life in the tropics.

The characteristic way in which all bugs develop is by a series of instars, or stages separated by skin changes. In the course of these the insect gradually takes on the characters of the adult and continues to feed and move about throughout its life without a break, contrasting with, for example, the pupa of a moth. The false pupa of the whiteflies is an interesting departure from the normal way in which bugs develop, and it closely parallels the true pupa of such insects as butterflies, bees and beetles. The differences are that the false pupa has much the same shape as the previous larval stage and it keeps feeding. It is also decorated with wax rods.

Imported killers

The greenhouse whitefly can be effectively controlled by the use of another exotic insect, the minute chalcid wasp *Encarsia formosa,* which probably also came from the tropics, although nobody is sure of its precise point of origin. This wasp is a parasite of the whitefly and was first noticed in a greenhouse at Elstree, in Hertfordshire, England, in 1926. A stock of it was bred up and was found to be effective in wiping out whitefly in greenhouses. Consignments of it were sent out all over Britain and also to Canada and Australia.

The parasite reproduces by parthenogenesis, that is, by the development of unfertilised eggs. The males are rare and apparently do not mate even when they occur. The female wasps lay their eggs in the larvae or 'scales' of the whitefly, and those that are parasitised turn black; this is useful as an indication that the parasite is being effective. To introduce the wasp, bunches of tomato leaves bearing parasitised scales are obtained and hung up in the greenhouse. Blackening of the scales is generally noticed 2–3 weeks after the introduction of the parasitised material. A night temperature of about 13°C/55°F is needed to maintain the wasps: good evidence that they are from warmer climates.

△ *A congregation of whitefly of the family Aleyrodidae. They are not, in fact, flies, but hemipteran, sap-sucking bugs.*

Whitefly

Whitefly are not flies at all but extremely small bugs very closely related to the aphids (p 69) and scale insects (p 2034). They are seldom more than ⅛ in. long and many are less than this. The adults look like minute white moths as they fly actively around. Their colour is due to a fine waxy powder which covers the body and wings. This is given out from the anus, which lies in a cavity overlaid by a tongue-shaped flap, or lingula, the cavity itself being covered by a lid, or operculum. Originally, the wax was probably given out as a waste substance, as in some other bugs, but in whiteflies this 'waste' is put to use, possibly as a protective covering. The majority of known whiteflies are tropical and they would largely escape notice but for the fact that some are serious pests of crops. Indeed, it is highly likely that the majority of whiteflies living today have yet to be discovered. The cabbage whitefly infects cabbages in Britain and other temperate countries, and the greenhouse whitefly is a tropical insect which establishes itself in glasshouses, attacking tomatoes, cucumbers and many other plants. It is believed to have come originally from Brazil. A third species, the citrus whitefly, is a pest of citrus fruits in the southern United States.

Harmful sapsucker

The cabbage whitefly congregates when young on the undersides of cabbage leaves where it breeds throughout the summer. In autumn the adults rise in clouds when disturbed and settle again like tiny snowflakes. Both the greenhouse and citrus species discolour and weaken the plants they infest by sucking their sap, in the same way as aphids, and like the aphids they cover the plants with sticky honeydew. On citrus fruit the honeydew promotes the growth of a fungus, the sooty mould *Meliola camelliae,* which so discolours the fruit that, even if it is not spoiled altogether, it has to be expensively washed for marketing. The reason why whiteflies and other bugs take in so much sap, in excess of their need for carbohydrates, is that they need other nutrients such as amino-acids, which are less concentrated in the sap.

Eggs laid in circles

The eggs are laid on the undersides of leaves, sometimes in a double layer, and are usually arranged in an arc or a circle, because when laying the female keeps her head in one place and moves her body round it. Each egg has a stalk and is laid upright, a batch of eggs looking rather like a group of minute pegs. The larvae are tiny and scale-like. They move about, feeding on the sap and excreting honeydew. They cast their skins three times and after the third moult the larva develops rods or filaments of wax all around itself. Then it stops feeding and settles down in a condition resembling that of the pupa of a higher insect. After a longer or shorter period of rest, varying with the species, the winged insect emerges fully developed.

phylum	**Arthropoda**
class	**Insecta**
order	**Hemiptera**
suborder	**Homoptera**
family	**Aleyrodidae**
genera & species	***Aleyrodes brassicae*** *cabbage whitefly* ***Dialeurodes citri*** *citrus whitefly* ***Trialeurodes vaporariorum*** *greenhouse whitefly others*

Whiting

A member of the cod family, the whiting is an important food fish and forms a considerable part of the catch of the North Sea trawlers. It reaches a length of 28 in., the females being slightly larger than the males. The whiting is easily distinguished by its silvery sides, the black spot at the base of each pectoral fin and by having only a very small inconspicuous barbel or none at all in most of the larger individuals. The snout is long and rather pointed with the longer upper jaw extending back to the front edge of the pupil. There are three soft-rayed dorsal fins and two anal. The colour varies on the back and the head from sandy to dark blue or green, but all whiting have the silvery sides and belly.

The whiting ranges from the North Sea off Iceland and Norway through the Irish Sea and the English Channel to the Mediterranean. In the Black Sea it is replaced by a subspecies.

Abundant in shallow waters

The whiting is very common throughout its range, being particularly abundant in the North and Irish Seas. Unlike most members of the cod family it lives mainly in shallow waters: it is most common at 36–330 ft and exceptionally goes below 4 000 ft. Sometimes whiting come close inshore and are caught in a few feet of water. Like all members of the cod family, whiting make considerable seasonal migrations within their range. Being a good fighter for its size it makes a good sporting fish for anglers. The record for one caught on rod and line off the British coast is 6 lb.

Eat anything small enough

Whiting feed principally in the daytime, mostly in midwater or just off the bottom. Their food consists mainly of smaller fish such as sprats, younger whiting, herring and sand eels but they will also take large quantities of crustaceans such as shrimps, prawns and crabs and occasionally cuttlefish, small squids and worms. Young whiting, which live mainly close to the shore, feed on shrimps, young shore crabs, amphipods, small gobies and sand eels.

△ *Mixed shoal of pout—with the deeper fins—and whiting. Both are eminently edible and provide consistent sport for the angler.*

A deadly shelter

In northern areas whiting spawn principally in April and May but they may begin as early as January in the south and continue into July in the north. Spawning takes place mainly in depths of 300 ft or less and sometimes in only 60 ft of water. This is in much shallower waters than either the cod or the haddock. The eggs resemble those of the cod and haddock but are smaller, averaging $\frac{1}{20}$ in. diameter. They are laid in great numbers and float at the surface. When hatched the young larva is about $\frac{1}{10}$ in. long. It drifts at the surface feeding on plankton. This is the most critical stage of its life, at the mercy of its numerous enemies. If it survives it grows fairly quickly and in its first year averages about 6 in., increasing to about 9 in. in its second year when it matures and to 12 in. in the third year. The females live for 7–8 years, reaching a length of $19\frac{1}{2}$–21 in. at this age.

Very young whiting, once they have reached a length of about $\frac{3}{4}$ in., sometimes

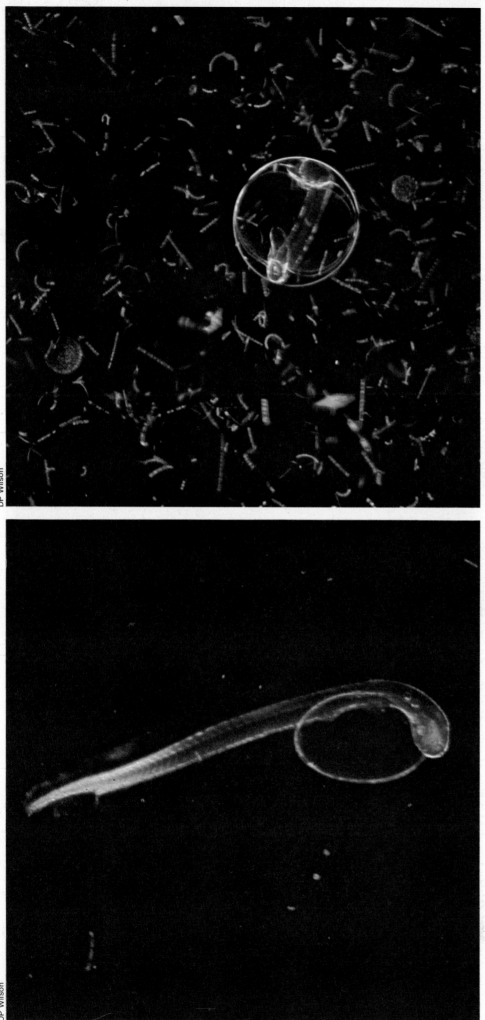

associate with jellyfish, particularly *Cyanea*, sheltering under the bell in small shoals and swimming among the stinging tentacles, enjoying the protection without apparently coming to any harm themselves. After reaching 2½ in. in length they sink to the bottom and are found in great numbers close to the shore, especially in sandy bays and estuaries.

Many enemies when young

The most perilous stage of the whiting's life is when it is first hatched and drifting at the surface. It is helpless against seabirds, predatory fish and adverse tides and currents. Although thousands of eggs are produced at a single spawning very few reach adulthood. In the British Isles, particularly during July and August, young whiting frequent the shrimping grounds off the Lancashire coast where thousands of them are destroyed each year through the operations of the shrimpers.

Fishery

There seems to be no evidence of overfishing of the whiting and particularly in the North Sea catches have been increasing in recent years. In 1952 the total European catch amounted to 73 000 tons and in 1963 to 185 000 tons. Most whiting are caught by trawl, by far the most effective and widely used of all fishing methods. It is very ancient, having been used in Britain as early as the reign of Edward III, when its use was prohibited because it destroyed too many small fish. Even today, although it has been greatly improved upon, the trawl is a very destructive means of fishing because in addition to taking in so many unmarketable small fish it ploughs up the sea-bed, killing the small bottom-living creatures on which so many fishes feed. The trawlers themselves have been greatly improved in recent years. Steam has given place to diesel engines enabling the ships to spend longer at sea and travel greater distances. Echosounding and underwater equipment, similar to that used in the Second World War to detect submarines, is now widely used to detect shoals of fish and the nets are constantly being improved in efficiency, strength and ease of handling.

class	**Pisces**
order	**Gadiformes**
family	**Gadidae**
genus & species	*Merlangus merlangus* *M. merlangus euxinus* *Black Sea whiting*

◁△ *Egg of whiting suspended in a mass of plant plankton, chain-form diatoms, and a golf-ball-like aggregation of the microscopic flagellate* **Phaeocystis** *(approx × 40).*
◁ *Minute early larva of a whiting. At this stage it drifts with the surface plankton, at the mercy of wind, tide and predators (× 40).*

Whydah

*The whydahs or widow-birds form a group of sparrow-like birds sometimes classed with the weaver finches, and sometimes with the large family of 'ploceid weavers' (see weaver, p 2586). The name is also, confusingly, given to the genus **Euplectes** which is related to the bishops, fodis and queleas in the 'ploceid weaver' family. Whatever the true relations of the whydahs, they form a distinct group of African, seed-eating birds that lay their eggs in the nests of weaver finches.*

There are about 11 species of whydah. The females are drab and sparrow-like throughout the year but in the breeding season the males have a special plumage which is usually shiny black, sometimes with very long tail feathers. The Senegal combassou or indigo finch is an example of a whydah without a long tail. In the breeding season the male of this species looks like a small blackbird, but the feathers have a bluish gloss and the bill is white. The male of the pin-tailed whydah, which is found throughout most of Africa south of the Sahara, measures 15 in. of which 9—10 in. is made up by the four central tail feathers. The breeding plumage is black and white, the tail, back and head being glossy black. The bill is pink. Another distinctive and widespread whydah is the paradise whydah which also has a 10in. tail but the two outer feathers are only half the length of the inner two. The plumage is black with pale brown underparts and neck but this description hardly conveys the appearance of the bird. JD Macdonald writes that 'one is astonished on first seeing a fully plumaged male in flight . . . for momentarily it is difficult to register the fact that it is a bird.'

Birds of open spaces

Whydahs live in the savannahs and plains of Africa rather than in wooded regions frequented by the weavers. Like the weavers, however, they form large flocks outside the breeding season, sometimes mixing with flocks of weavers and weaver finches. Some species are also found around towns and villages. Whydahs are predominantly seed eaters but they also take insects. They feed mainly on the ground, searching for small seeds by scratching with their feet.

Cuckoos in paradise dress

For a long time the breeding habits of the whydahs were unknown and only a very few nests were ever described. It was suspected that these descriptions were based on mistaken identifications, and quite rightly so, because it was later shown that whydahs do not build nests. They are parasites, like cuckoos, and lay their eggs in the nests of their near relatives the weaver finches.

In the whydahs there is no bond between male and female, which is not surprising as once mating is completed the male's role is ended. The males are polygamous and are aggressive towards each other. Many have elaborate courtship displays, so rivalling the birds of paradise in their behaviour as well as in plumage. The male paradise whydah clears a patch of ground about 4 ft across and prances about on it to attract females. Others, such as the pin-tailed whydah, perform display flights, ascending 100—200 ft then fluttering slowly down with the long tail waving.

Each species of whydah usually lays its eggs in the nests of a particular species of weaver finch. In normal circumstances only

▽ *Elongated glory: a male pin-tailed whydah from Africa. His 9—10in. tail comes into its own during courtship flights.*

one egg is laid in each nest and the host's eggs are not destroyed, but if a second whydah lays in a nest where there is already one whydah egg she will destroy one of the weaver finch eggs. Both the host's and parasite's eggs are white, yet the whydah can recognise, and destroy, the host's eggs.

The perfect mimic

The whydahs possess a remarkable mechanism to ensure that their offspring are successfully brought up by the foster parents. This is necessary because of the manner in which the young weaver finches are reared. They are fed by the parents thrusting their bills into the chicks' mouths and regurgitating semi-digested food. To guide the parents each chick has a pattern of black markings in the mouth and bright spots around the bill. They also have special begging calls. The markings and calls vary between the species and a weaver finch only feeds chicks with the correct markings and calls. It is therefore essential that the whydah chicks should mimic the recognition signals of their foster parents' chicks. Each whydah species has evolved the mouth markings and begging calls of its particular host and the fledglings even have plumage resembling that of the host fledgling.

Because of the need of the whydah chick to resemble the host chick it is essential that the female whydah lays her eggs in the nests of the correct weaver finches. This happens in cuckoos in which the egg markings mimic those of the host species (see weaver, p 2586) and it seems that the female cuckoo is somehow able to recognise nests of the species in which she herself was raised. In the whydahs, it seems that the male also plays a part in ensuring that the eggs are laid in the right nest. There are several very similar races of paradise whydah, some of which live in the same areas. Each race parasitises a different weaver finch, so it is essential for female paradise whydahs to mate with the right race of male, otherwise the hybrid offspring will not mimic the host. Recognition is based on song. Incredibly, male paradise whydahs mimic the songs of their hosts, so that, for example, a male narrow-tailed paradise whydah sings a song almost indistinguishable from that of the melba finch *Pytilia melba* which reared it. The song attracts female paradise whydahs which were also reared by melba finches and are conditioned to laying their eggs in melba finch nests.

class	**Aves**
order	**Passeriformes**
family	**Ploceidae**
genera & species	***Hypochera chalybeata*** *Senegal combassou* ***Vidua macroura*** *pin-tailed whydah* ***V. paradisaea*** *paradise whydah* *others*

◁ *One of the genus **Euplectes**, a link between the 'ploceid weavers' and the whydahs—* ***E. progne*** *the giant whydah, or sakabula.*

Wild cat

Wild cat

The wild cat of Europe and Asia resembles the domesticated tabby but is more heavily built. The average length is about 2 ft 9 in. of which 11 in. is tail, but there is a record from Scotland of one that reached 3 ft 9 in. total length and there is an unconfirmed report of one shot in Scotland that measured 4¼ ft. The weight of a male averages 11 lb but may be as much as 15 lb and that of the female 8½ lb with a maximum of 10 lb; one wild cat from the Carpathians weighed nearly 33 lb. The wild cat has a squarish, robust head and a stouter and longer body than the normal domestic cat. The thick bushy tail is relatively shorter than in the domestic cat and is ringed, ending in a long black tip.

The limbs, too, are longer than those of the tame cat.

The fur is long, soft and thick, and is mainly yellowish-grey but there is a good deal of variation. Individuals differ in their dark brown markings, some having vertical stripes running down the sides, while in others these are broken up to form spots. Since there seems to have been considerable cross-breeding with feral domestic cats some of the variations in the pattern of the coat may be due to this.

In Europe the wild cat is now confined chiefly to the mountains, especially in the Balkans, and in the British Isles it is restricted mainly to the Scottish Highlands north of the Great Glen, where its numbers are said to be increasing. It also extends into Asia Minor with related species in central Asia.

Wild and inaccessible home

The wild cat lives on very lonely and inaccessible mountainsides or in wooded places, hiding during the day among rocks and prowling far and wide at night in search of prey. It hunts alone or in pairs, being most active at dawn and at dusk, although in the autumn there is a tendency to hunt by day. The home range covers an area of 150–175 acres which is defended by the male, who may wander well outside this in search of food in winter or in the breeding season. Like the domestic cat, the wild cat will shelter from the rain but loves to bask in the sun, on a bough or a rocky ledge.

The wild cat is one of the fiercest and most destructive of the cat family and when hard pressed its strength and ferocity are remarkable. Some so-called wild cats are feral domesticated cats and although these do not attack human beings they will fight capture as furiously as the true wild cat.

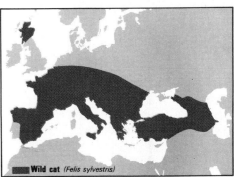

Wild cat (*Felis sylvestris*)

◁ *Feline ferocity: a Scottish wild cat at bay, giving final warning before attack.*

Persecuted by man

Although the wild cat now has few natural enemies as most of the large predators in its range have been wiped out, it nevertheless has always had man's hand against it because of its destructiveness to poultry and lambs. Many years ago, when it was widespread over England, the wild cat was hunted for sport.

Unsolved problems

We can be fairly certain that the domestic cat is not descended from the European wild cat. As suggested on p 390 we cannot be sure whether the domestic cat came from the jungle cat or the African bush cat. Moreover, we cannot be sure that the jungle cat and even less the bush cat does not belong to the same species as the European wild cat. In any case they look very much alike and they behave in much the same way, and above all, the kittens of all three species are said to be virtually untameable.

To say that the wild cat kittens are untameable, even if taken into captivity before their eyes are open and hand-reared, is to risk the challenge from one or more people who claim to have hand-reared and tamed a kitten from a wild cat mother. The probability is that the remark is acceptable as a generalisation, but to all generalisations there are exceptions. With all wild mammal babies we know that the chance of successful taming is increased the earlier they are taken from the mother and hand-fed before the eyes open. Moreover, in every litter there will be one that is more tameable than the others. Possibly therefore the domestication of the cat from its wild ancestor depended on selecting the more tameable kittens and hand-rearing them almost from birth. However, there is evidence from the personal stories of a few who have tried this which suggests that when a wild cat kitten has been tamed, it can be handled by the person who hand-reared it, and by nobody else. So it is indeed remarkable that the cat was domesticated in the first place, although some insight is gained into the independent nature of the domestic cat.

The voice of the wild cat ranges from a meeow, a growl when angry and a purr when pleased, to the typical small cat scream or caterwaul on occasion. C St John writing in 1845 says: 'I have heard their wild and unearthly cry echo far into the quiet night as they answer and call to each other. I do not know a more harsh and unpleasant cry than that of the wild cat.'

Poultry and lambs in peril

The wild cat's main food is mountain hares, grouse and rabbits but it will eat any small mammal or bird it can catch as well as fish and insects. It can kill a roe fawn and create havoc among poultry or lambs, this being the main reason why it has been wiped out in much of its former range.

Fierce mother

There are two breeding seasons, in early March and again in late May or early June,

the litters of 4–5 kittens being born in May and August respectively. Very occasionally there is a third litter in December or January, but it is suspected that these may have been from a domestic-wild cat cross. The gestation is 63 days. The kittens are born in a nest made by the female in some remote rock cleft or hollow tree, well away from the male, who may kill his own young. The kittens' fur is a light ground colour with greyish-brown tabby markings. The female is very fierce while she has her kittens in the nest and will attack any animal, no matter what its size, that dares to intrude. Even the kittens will spit and fight if handled. Very few have been taken alive and all are said to have proved untameable. They leave the nest at 4–5 weeks old but do not go hunting with the mother until 10–12 weeks old and they are not weaned until they are 4 months. They leave the mother to fend for themselves when 5 months old.

class	**Mammalia**
order	**Carnivora**
family	**Felidae**
genus & species	*Felis sylvestris*

Wobbegong

Wobbegongs, or carpet sharks, are most unusual sharks. Unlike most sharks the wobbegong uses cunning instead of speed to obtain its food. Resting on the sea bottom it looks like a rock overgrown with seaweed, a perfect camouflage to enable it to pounce on unsuspecting victims. Most wobbegongs are small but some of the larger species grow to a length of 6—8 ft; the largest of all is **Orectolobus maculatus**, which ranges from Queensland to South and West Australia and Tasmania, reaching 10½ ft.

The wobbegong is quite unlike the usual shark in shape. It has a stout, thick-set, flattened body with a very broad head and a blunt rounded snout ending in a wide straight mouth. Its teeth are slender and pointed, those in the centre of the mouth being the largest. Its eyes are small with folds of skin below them, and the wide, oblique slits of the spiracles are situated behind the eyes and lower down on the head. The last three or four external gill-clefts on each side open above the

bases of the pectoral fins, which are broad and sometimes rounded. The two dorsal fins are comparatively small. The anal fin either reaches to or is actually joined at its base to the lower lobe of the tailfin which is long and asymmetrical with a notch in the end. The skin is covered with small rough denticles. The colour of wobbegongs varies with different species and individuals but the ground colour is usually brown, yellowish or grey with distinctive mottled or striped markings of a lighter or darker colour. What distinguishes the wobbegong from any other shark is the fringe of fleshy lobes or flaps of skin around the sides of the head and mouth which resemble fronds of seaweed when the shark is at rest.

There are about five species of wobbegong living in the seas around China, Japan and east and south Australia.

Sluggish existence

The wobbegong lives an inactive life spending most of its time lying hidden on the sea bottom among the rocks and weeds, only coming to life when a fish passes by for it to snap up. It is further concealed by waving its flaps of skin so they look even more like

seaweed. Its heavy body is not built for speed like most other sharks that hunt their prey, but its perfect camouflage gives it an equally effective means of obtaining food. Wobbegongs do not need to keep moving, as do typical sharks, in order to breathe. They draw water into the gill chamber through the spiracles, in much the same way as skates and rays.

Wobbegongs are not aggressive and under normal circumstances are not considered very dangerous to humans. Nevertheless, cases have been known of their attacking people wading in shallow water. Their long pointed teeth are said to be perfectly capable of biting off a man's foot but they very seldom attack unless stepped on or provoked in some other way.

The wobbegong has little or no value as food but its colourful variegated skin makes it valuable in the shark-leather industry.

Snapping up fish

The wobbegong feeds on any fish or crustacean which comes within reach of its jaws as it lies hidden on the sea bottom. It has even been known to snap fish from the spears of underwater fishermen.

Little-known breeding

Very little is known about the breeding habits of the wobbegong. Like the nurse sharks it is ovoviviparous and produces large numbers of young at each birth.

A fisherman attacked

Despite the fact that the wobbegong is not considered a very dangerous shark an instance has been recorded in New South Wales, Australia, of one attacking a spear-fisherman who was fishing in Shellharbour in 1953. He was using a snorkel and wearing an underwater mask with a bright metal band. He was trying to spear a dying grouper and running out of shafts he surfaced and borrowed another gun. As he shot a spear into the fish it came out of its cave followed by a large, brown wobbegong shark with three or four tentacles hanging from its lip. The spear-fisherman swam quickly for about 15 yards but the shark rushed at him to attack. It is well known that bright objects and metal attract sharks and the wobbegong was obviously going for the mask with its bright metal band. It tore away the face piece and snapped off the snorkel. The rush of the attack was so great that both the shark and the fisherman were hurled from the water, enabling the fisherman to escape with injuries only under his chin and to his face and nose.

class	**Selachii**
order	**Pleurotremata**
family	**Orectolobidae**
genus & species	**Orectolobus maculatus** *others*

◁ *Wobbegong* **Orectolobus ogilbyi** *lurks, nearly perfectly camouflaged, in its Barrier Reef niche. Unique among sharks, the seaweed-like fringe which breaks the outline of the mouth is clearly visible in this shot.*

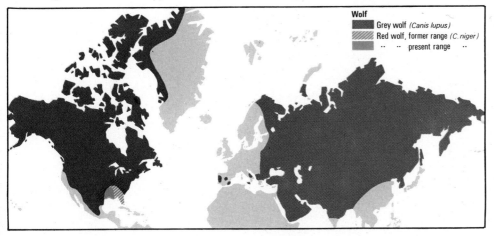

Wolf

Thought by many to be at least one of the possible ancestors of the domestic dog, the wolf was once widespread over Europe, most of Asia and North America and had a range probably greater than any other land mammal. Today, there are two distinct species of wolf, the grey or timber wolf which is still found in the wilder parts of northern Europe, Asia and North America and the red wolf which is restricted to the south-central United States. There are numerous local races, however, differing in size and colour.

The grey wolf is the larger of the two, with a head and body length averaging 42−54 in. and a tail of 11½−22 in. The height at the shoulders is up to 38 in. The weight varies from about 60−150 lb. The grey wolf tends to be heavier in the more northern parts of its range—one shot in east-central Alaska weighed 175 lb. The red wolf is more slender, weighing on average 33 lb, occasionally 70−80 lb.

Both species are dog-like in appearance. They have large heads with erect rounded ears and long muzzles with strong jaws which contain 6−7 cheek teeth on each side, including a well-developed carnassial. The limbs are long and slender with four toes on the hindfoot and five on the forefoot, each bearing non-retractile claws. When angry, wolves erect the long hair on the nape of the neck, so that it looks like a mane. There is a scent gland on the upper side of the tail near its base which is used for recognition.

The colour of the grey wolf varies considerably over its range but it is usually grey, sprinkled with black apart from the legs and underparts which are yellowish-white. Black and light-coloured phases occur quite commonly. On the Arctic coast of Alaska and in western Canada, wolves are sometimes white throughout the year but more usually they are a mixture of white and grey tinged with brown. The red wolf is more tawny and sometimes small ones look like coyotes.

△ Wolves travel a great deal, and although a grey or timber wolf does not attain great speeds, its stamina enables it to keep a steady pace and journey for miles at a time.
▷ Overleaf. Both intelligence and a high degree of co-operation are required for animals to hunt in groups; only the mammals have these qualifications, and of them the wolves are among the most efficient. Here a pack manoeuvres in an attempt to make a strong adult moose panic, bolt, and thus expose its vulnerable flanks to the combined jaws of the pack. They are not always successful; a 16-strong pack studied on Isle Royale in Lake Superior, Canada, where this picture was taken, harassed an average of 16 moose for every one they killed. The wolves attack adult moose only in the winter, when deep snow gives the hunters the advantage.

Savage and intelligent

The wolf is a ruthless and ferocious carnivore. It is also very courageous and has great fighting ability, intelligence and endurance. It lives in open country and forests, hunting by day and hiding at night among rocks, under fallen trees or in holes dug in the ground. Wolves sometimes hunt singly or in pairs but more often they move in a family party or pack of from three to two dozen individuals. A single large wolf can bring down and kill a large steer but a pack can tackle much larger animals such as moose or elk. Although a wolf runs at an average speed of only 22−24 mph, reaching a maximum of 28 mph for short distances, it has remarkable powers of endurance and can keep up a loping run for mile after mile, running right through the night if necessary. It has greater powers of endurance than most large game animals and so it can usually outrun its prey. It travels widely and there is a record of a red wolf in Oklahoma which covered 125 miles in two weeks, crossing four mountain ranges. The wolf is

Wolf
Grey wolf *(Canis lupus)*
Red wolf, former range *(C. niger)*
present range

△ *That lean and hungry look: timber wolf in alert pose. The wolf would seem, at first sight, the most probable ancestral dog, but modern opinion favours an extinct wild dog.*

a good swimmer when necessary, sometimes pursuing deer into the water.

The wolves make use of pathways through the territory, which is usually in open country, often incorporating game trails and cattle tracks in these hunting routes which sometimes cover more than 100 miles and have numerous 'latrines' which also function as scent posts and vantage points on high ground for observation.

Large feeder

The wolf is an enormous feeder. It can eat ⅕ of its body weight at one meal and then go without food for a considerable time, rather like a snake. Although it will kill large animals such as caribou, musk-oxen, deer, moose and horses, much of its food is made up of small animals such as mice, rabbits and squirrels. Fish and crabs are sometimes taken, as well as carrion. When natural food is short the wolf will take to killing any domestic livestock and poultry within its range and will even resort to man-killing when driven to it by starvation.

A large family

The breeding season is usually from January to March with a gestation of 60–63 days. There are 5–14 cubs in a litter, usually 7, born in a den prepared by the female. At birth the cubs are blind with a sooty brown fur, except in the Arctic where the white colour phase predominates and the cubs' fur is light blue or dull slate. The eyes open 5–9 days after birth and at 18 months the cubs are well-grown. Both parents teach the cubs to hunt and kill prey and the family may keep together for some time. The males are fully mature in 3 years and females in 2. They are thought to mate for life.

Slaughtered by man

Over many centuries the wolf's chief enemy has been man. Constant efforts have been made to exterminate it because of its destructiveness to domestic stock and even to human life. Numerous methods have been used to kill it, including poison, steel traps, shooting and hunting by dogs and it says much for the wolf's cunning and endurance that it still survives over much of its former range. Indeed, it is only the encroachment of human settlement on its habitat that has been most effective in reducing its numbers.

The wolf in legend

From earliest times the wolf has been depicted in literature and legend as a symbol of savagery, courage and endurance. Beowulf, the legendary Teutonic hero, and many Anglo-Saxon kings and nobles incorporated 'wolf' into their names as an indication of their fighting prowess and in North America the Indians used the name for their most powerful warriors. Yet, strangely enough, there have been many stories, from way back in history, of wolves that have raised human children from infancy, lovingly looking after them and protecting them from other predators. The most famous story is that of Romulus, the legendary founder of Rome and his twin brother Remus, but in more recent times there is a story from India, purported to be true, of a child raised by a wolf until she was about 9 years old.

class	**Mammalia**
order	**Carnivora**
family	**Canidae**
genus & species	***Canis lupus*** *grey or timber wolf* **C. niger** *red wolf*

Wolf spider

Wolf spiders, like the carnivores after which they are named, run their prey down instead of making a silken snare like so many other spiders. There are, however, a few species that use silk to line their burrows or make silk tubes from which to pounce on their prey.

They are small to medium-sized spiders, the largest being less than 1 in. long in the body with legs also 1 in. long. They are dark or drab in colour, and their bodies are covered with a pile of short bristles. They have strong jaws. Their most characteristic feature is the three rows of eyes on the head; four small eyes in front, just above the base of the jaws, then two larger eyes in each of the two succeeding rows, all simple, as in other arachnids.

*Wolf spiders are widespread across all the continents except Antarctica. The total number of species is hard to estimate: there are about 125 in North America, and 50 in Europe. The tarantula of southern Europe **Lycosa** is a wolf spider.*

Wolf-like in many ways

Wolf spiders are often numerous, especially among leaf litter. They tend to be more active at night or under overcast conditions, but they can sometimes be seen in large numbers by day, running over dead leaves, probably because they were disturbed by someone walking over the litter. They shelter by day in small burrows dug in soft earth. Some species line the burrow with silk, while others also have a silken tube running out a short way from the mouth of the burrow. The silk is never used as a snare, but more as an ambush. The food, as with most spiders, is small insects, which the wolf spiders pursue and grab with their strong jaws. They then chew their prey to a pulp and suck the juices through a very small mouth, too small to admit any but the smallest particles.

Wooing by waving

Wolf spiders have relatively keen sight and courtship is conducted by visual signals. A male ready to breed sets out in search of a female. He stations himself in front of her and begins to wave his long palps up and down like semaphore arms. These are usually black and are conspicuous against the drab body. In some species, parts of the

△ *Beloved burden: the female wolf spider — this one is **Pisaura mirabilis** — is very attached to her cocoon and will substitute some other similar object if it is removed from her care.*

front pair of legs are also black and these are also held up and waved. The males of many species vibrate this front pair of legs; in other species the male may tremble in the legs and the abdomen. If the female is not receptive at first she may be induced to respond later by the sight of these movements in the male. She may then face the male and signal back in like manner. Finally the two mate by the male placing his sperm, previously deposited in the pedipalp, into the female's genital pore.

The female lays her eggs in a spherical or lens-shaped silk cocoon, specially spun for the purpose. She attaches this cocoon to the rear end of her abdomen and carries it around with her wherever she goes. Should the cocoon become detached she turns and retrieves it, fastening it again to her abdomen. In experiments, designed to test her devotion to the cocoon, it was found that if the cocoon is taken away and a small white object such as a pith ball, or a pellet of screwed up blotting paper, placed on the ground near the spider she will retrieve this.

△ *About hatching time, in June or July, the female* **Pisaura mirabilis** *detaches her cocoon and spins a tent over it, by which she stands guard. Clustered together inside, the young complete the final stages of development, including two moults, and then disperse.*

Family bus

When the eggs hatch the spiderlings remain for a short while in the cocoon until it splits, under favourable weather conditions. They then climb onto the mother's back and are transported by her. In some species the brood is so numerous the spiderlings cover the mother's back several layers deep. So far as we know the spiderlings do not feed during this time. Should one fall off the mother does not halt for it to regain its position on her back, or do anything to assist it. The spiderling must either quickly climb up one of her legs, to reach her back, or be left behind to perish. This is in sharp contrast to the solicitude she shows for the eggs in the cocoon. She will seek shelter when it is raining, to preserve the cocoon, and should it get wet she will, at the earliest opportunity, tilt her head and body downwards to hold the cocoon up to the sun to dry it. 'Solicitude' is probably the wrong word because there is nothing intelligent or deliberate about these acts. They are all automatic responses to circumstances.

Two deadly enemies

The drab colouring of wolf spiders, their mainly nocturnal habits and their use of burrows into which they can retire gives them a fair degree of immunity from enemies. There are, however, two important enemies. The first is the mantisfly, which preys on the eggs while they are still in the cocoon. Hunting wasps are the second danger. They paralyse the spiders and use them to feed their larvae. These hunting wasps fly low over the ground on a zigzag course, searching for prey. When a wasp is over the burrow of a wolf spider it lands and starts to dig. Once the wasp is inside the burrow the spider becomes easy prey.

WS Bristowe has described how he touched a wolf spider *Arctosa perita* sitting at the mouth of its burrow with the tip of a fine grass stem. The spider grabbed the silk on one side of the opening and pulled it across, like a curtain, until only a small slit was left, which it then closed by spinning silk criss-cross over it. We can suppose this is what it would do to keep out a wasp.

Mother's clear vision

The eyes are more important to wolf spiders than to web-spinning spiders. When a female is loaded with her brood of spiderlings they spread in a solid layer, or layers, across her back and onto her head. Yet you never see any of the babies covering the mother's eyes. This seems like some remarkable instinct which makes the spiderlings draw back when in danger of covering their mother's eyes. When we watch carefully, however, we see that every now and then one or more spiderlings are pressed forward by the mob, so almost blindfolding the mother. The moment this happens the mother passes one of her palps over her head, like someone brushing back their hair, and casually pushes the erring spiderlings away from her eyes.

phylum	**Arthropoda**
class	**Arachnida**
order	**Araneae**
families	**Lycosidae**
	Pisauridae

Wolverine

The wolverine, or glutton, is the largest of the weasel family. It has been aptly referred to by one writer as the super-weasel; yet its appearance is not that of a weasel, marten or stoat, but rather of a bear or badger. A full-grown male may be up to 4 ft long, including nearly a foot of tail, stand 14—17 in. at the shoulder and weigh 30—60 lb. The females are smaller and lighter. The wolverine is powerfully built, thick-bodied with short legs set widely apart and ending in broad powerful paws armed with long sharp claws. It has a shaggy coat of thick dense fur, very dark brown above, with a pale brown band on the sides and dark brown below.

The wolverine ranges across the Arctic and sub-Arctic regions of Europe and Asia and in North America from the Arctic to the northern United States.

Ferocity and courage

Wolverines live in the cold evergreen forests from 800 to 13 000 ft above sea-level. They are solitary except during the breeding season, inhabiting very large but definite territories. They hunt mainly at night although they tend to have a 3- or 4-hourly rhythm of alternate activity and rest. They do not burrow or make any permanent home but use whatever shelter is available in the particular locality they are hunting. Where they use man-made shelters in this way they may tear down the timbers of a cabin to effect an entry and also wreck the contents, consuming what food they need and carrying other articles away. This has given them a false reputation for wanton destructiveness.

The wolverine cannot move with speed and, unlike the smaller members of its family, has little skill in stalking. At most, it may hide behind a rock in a kind of ambush or drop from a branch of a tree onto a victim's back. Mainly, it depends for survival on its unusual courage in driving other predators from their food. The wolverine

bares its teeth, raises the hair on its back, erects its bushy tail and emits a low growl. Even bears have been driven from a carcase by such a display. It has remarkably strong teeth and jaws and is said to crack large bones to powder, to snap branches up to 2 in. diameter with ease and to have bitten a lump out of a rifle butt. The more reliable reports suggest, unless disturbed with young, that it is not aggressive towards man.

Trappers' tales

Among the exaggerated stories about the wolverine is its alleged high skill not only in avoiding the traps of the fur trapper but in robbing those in which marten and fox have been caught. When satiated it is said to exude its musk on the remaining carcases to prevent any other beast taking them. It has even been said that parent wolverines teach their young how to spring traps. The truth seems to be that it does

▽ *Casual encounter: powerful enough to fear nothing in its Swedish National Park home, a wolverine pauses to size up the photographer.*

sometimes rob traps and there may have been occasions when a whole line of traps has been cleared but, as a rule, the depredations are not as wholesale as most accounts suggest. As for skill in avoiding traps, this seems to be explained by the small size of the traps used. Wolverines are usually caught by the toes in marten traps and often escape leaving a toe or two behind. There seems to be no evidence that they can avoid, or escape, the larger traps set deliberately for them.

A libellous name

Its diet is a wide one. Mice, rats, small mammals of many kinds, eggs, ground-nesting birds, ducks and even snails are included. Above all, carrion, especially the kills of other carnivores, is eaten. It is reputed to be powerful enough to kill a reindeer or even a moose or elk and to drag a carcase three times its own weight for some distance over rough ground. Uneaten food is cached, either covered with soil or snow or wedged in the fork of a tree. A wolverine has a reputation for eating more than any other carnivore—hence its name of glutton—but probably the many stories about its excessive feeding habits are also exaggerations. Indeed, some of them take no account of the size of the animal's stomach.

Possible delayed implantation

The young, usually 2 or 3, occasionally 5, are born from February to May. The ges-tation period seems to be uncertain, the records varying from 60–120, or even 183 days, suggesting that delayed implantation occurs. The young are born in a hollow tree, among rocks or even in a snow drift. They have thick woolly fur at birth and are weaned at 8–10 weeks. They stay with their mother for as long as 2 years, then she drives them away to find their own territories and fend for themselves. They are sexually mature at 4 years of age and in captivity have been known to live for 16 years.

Persecuted by man

Being so powerful the wolverine has little to fear from natural enemies. It has, however, been persecuted by man for its destructiveness and also because of its reputation for killing reindeer. For over 100 years attempts have been made in Norway to stamp out the wolverine and premiums have been paid for each one destroyed. The eskimos hunt it for its fur as this does not hold moisture and then freeze, so it is invaluable for trimming the hoods of their parkas. Although its numbers have been reduced everywhere by persecution it is still not uncommon in parts of its range.

Exaggerated beliefs

One of the many stories of the wolverine concerns its stratagem for catching deer, or other large prey. The animal is said to climb into a tree carrying a quantity of moss in its mouth. When a deer approached the wolverine would let the moss fall. Should the deer stop to eat it the wolverine would then drop onto its back, fix itself firmly between the antlers and tear out its victim's eyes. Following this, either from pain or to rid itself of its tormentor, the deer would bang its head against a tree until it fell dead.

As alleged proof of their amazing strength we have the 18th century account from Churchill, on Hudson Bay, of some provisions hidden by several of the Hudson Bay Company's servants in the top of a wood-pile. On their return from Christmas festivities, the wood-pile, over 70 yd round, had been thrown down and scattered about. And this 'notwithstanding some of the trees with which it was constructed were as much as two men could carry.' The large quantity of provisions had been consumed, or carried away, except for the sacks of flour and cereals, which had been ripped to shreds.

class	**Mammalia**
order	**Carnivora**
family	**Mustelidae**
genus & species	*Gulo gulo*

▽ *Profile of a powerful predator: a wolverine shows its strong head and claws as it looks out from a snowy vantage point.*

Wombat

Wombat

Like its nearest relative, the koala, the wombat looks like a bear, but it is more like a badger in its habits so it is often called 'badger' in Australia. Its head and body length varies from 27 to 47 in. and its weight from 33 to 80 lb. It is thickset with little or no tail, its legs are short and strong and its toes are armed with stout claws used in digging. The wombat's teeth are unlike those of other marsupials, being more similar to those of rodents. The 24 teeth are rootless and there are two incisors in both upper and lower jaws, like those of a beaver. There are traces of cheek pouches.

The two genera of wombats each contain a single species. The common or coarse-haired wombat lives in the hilly or mountainous coastal regions of south-eastern Australia and on Tasmania and Flinders Island in the Bass Strait. It is the larger of the two and has a naked muzzle, rounded ears and coarse fur ranging from a yellowish buff to dark brown or black.

The soft-furred or hairy-nosed wombat lives in the sandy or limestone coastal country and drier inland areas in the southern half of South Australia. It was once plentiful in the hilly parts of inland southern Queensland but it is probably nearing extinction in this area. It is distinguished from the common wombat by its smaller size and larger skull bones, and by having a haired nose and relatively pointed ears. The fur is soft and silky, the upperparts a grizzled-grey and the underparts white or grey.

Shy and nocturnal

Both species of wombats are nocturnal and shy and therefore difficult to observe in the wild. They sleep by day in burrows dug out with the powerful claws of their forefeet, the soil being thrust back with the hindfeet. The burrows are large, usually 10−15 ft long or as much as 100 ft at times, and one series of burrows is reported to have been $\frac{1}{2}$ mile long and 60 yd across. There is a sleeping chamber at the end of the burrow which contains a nest of bark. The entrance

◁ *Rounded ears, a naked muzzle and larger size are the hallmarks of this coarse-haired wombat, in contrast with its smaller relation, the hairy-nosed wombat (previous page).*

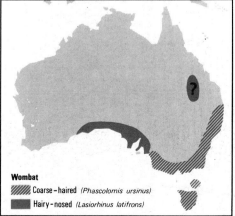

Wombat
Coarse-haired (Phascolomis ursinus)
Hairy-nosed (Lasiorhinus latifrons)

2629

△ *Greedy nibbler: the wombat tears up grass roots with its clawed forefeet to expose the tasty bases of grass stems and other roots.*

to the burrow is large and arched and a few yards away there is usually a shallow depression scraped in the surface of the ground, at the base of a tree, where the wombat goes to bask in the morning sun. Wombats are solitary except in the breeding season and quite inoffensive to man unless interfered with, although a female has been reported to attack someone in defence of her young. Although heavily built they are quick in their movements and can run swiftly for short distances. The only sound heard from a wombat is a hoarse grunting cough, rather like that made by a large kangaroo.

Wombats are easily kept in captivity and make affectionate and amusing pets. One is recorded as living for 26 years in captivity.

Diet of grass

There are often well-defined paths leading from the wombats' burrows to feeding areas in open country. Their food is mainly grass and roots and occasionally the inner bark of certain trees and fungi. They tear out and grasp the grass stems with their forefeet and they sometimes damage pasture and crops near settled areas.

One young in the pouch

During May to July the female gives birth to one young which is carried at first in the pouch, in the usual way of marsupials. Later

it runs free, but stays with the mother until the end of the year. During this time she feeds it on sword grass, pulling out the stems singly and dropping them on the ground so that the youngster can feed on the tender bases.

Man the chief enemy

The wombat has few natural enemies but it has suffered severely at the hands of man. In many areas it has disappeared entirely. Although its skin is not used commercially the aborigines make string out of the fur of the hairy-nosed wombat, coiling it round their hair. Wombats have been ruthlessly banished from settlements from early days because of their habit of tearing down fences to reach the grass in sheep pastures or cultivated crops of various kinds. Another similarity with badgers is that they have been killed for their hams. Their burrows have been eradicated because of the danger to horse riders and because rabbits sheltering in them could not easily be destroyed.

Resembling a badger

The first account of the common wombat in New South Wales was supplied by a former convict, James Wilson, in the 18th century, while on a journey into the southern highlands across the Nepean River. His account was written down by one of his companions, a young servant to Governor Hunter. When evidently near the present town of Bargo on January 26, 1798: 'We saw several sorts of

dung of different animals, one of which Wilson called Whom-batt, which is an animal about 20 inches high, with short legs and a thick body with a large head, round ears, and very small eyes, is very fat, and has much the appearance of a badger.'

As has been said before in previous articles many marsupials resemble closely in appearance and habits well-known animals in other parts of the world. The wombat is no exception with its marked resemblance to the badger. Although the wombat shows some characters of the koala and possums it is so unlike them in other features, particularly in feeding, that it has been classed in a family on its own. In the past wombats have not excited much interest and have therefore received little attention but they are quite as interesting zoologically as the koala and other marsupials, and it would be a pity if their remaining numbers were allowed to diminish any further. In view of the very great similarity to the badgers of the northern hemisphere, it would be of unusual interest for a complete study to be made of the wombat.

class	**Mammalia**
order	**Marsupialia**
family	**Phascolomidae**
genera & species	*Lasiorhinus latifrons* soft-furred or hairy-nosed wombat *Phascolomis ursinus* common or coarse-haired wombat

Wood ant

The wood ant is noted for the huge mounds it builds over its underground nest, transporting quantities of pine needles and twigs to do so. It lives in Europe in open woodlands or on heaths with clumps of trees. Wood ants are red with a black abdomen and they have a large scale on the 'waist'. The workers are $\frac{1}{6}-\frac{2}{5}$ in. long, and the queens are $\frac{1}{2}$ in. or more long, the males being only slightly smaller than the queens. The meadow ant or hairy wood ant, sometimes regarded as a distinct species, and sometimes as a subspecies of the wood ant, is darker in colour than the wood ant, and more bristly. It nests in more open country. The habits of only the common wood ant are described here.

A spreading city

The nest is usually built around a tree stump, but as nests may persist for many years the stump often disappears due to decay. The part of the nest above ground is made of small twigs and leaf stalks or pine needles and is really the roof or thatch of the nest, the greater part of which is underground. The thatch keeps out rain and it also keeps the temperature of the nest equable in very hot or cold weather. In an old colony it may be 5 ft high and 10 ft in diameter. Below the mound there is a large rounded pit filled with a mixture of leaf

mould and earth. Below this excavated channels slant downwards. In winter the ants retire to these channels, hibernating in clusters of several thousand individuals, each cluster having two or three queens at its centre. During summer the whole nest is occupied and open galleries are maintained throughout the mound as well as in the underground part of the nest.

The openings to the exterior are closed with twigs at night and guarded by sentinel ants by day. The worker ants stream in and out, carrying food, and materials for the thatch which is constantly being added to. Visible tracks, from which leaves and other obstacles have been cleared, run out from the nest and can sometimes be followed for over 50 yd. They lead to foraging grounds, trees on which large numbers of aphids are living, and to other nests. The wood ant nests in an area of woodland are usually interconnected like towns. Some are small and are obviously satellites of a large nest nearby; others have an independent existence, but the ants are not hostile to the ants from other nests in the vicinity.

Durable dynasties

Inside the nest the workers are concerned with feeding the queens and the larvae, taking over eggs from the queens and carrying larvae and pupae about to parts where the temperature and humidity are best for them. The pupae are contained in whitish oval cocoons about as large as the ants. These are the so-called 'ants' eggs' some-

△ *Collected by the carnivorous wood ants, a battered brimstone butterfly is borne back to the nest by a team of workers.*

times used as food for cage birds and fish in aquaria. The real eggs of the ants are microscopic in size. When a pupa is due to hatch workers tear open the cocoon and help the occupant out. If undisturbed a wood ants' nest may go on indefinitely: new queens are constantly recruited.

Founding new nests

Wood ant males and queens are winged, but there is no marriage flight as in many smaller kinds of ants. Mating takes place on the surface of the nest or on the ground nearby, usually in June or July. After mating the queen breaks off her wings and then may do one of three things. Her most usual course is simply to go back into the nest where she lived as a larva and add her eggs to those of her mother, sisters and 'aunts'. On the other hand, she may set out from her home after mating, accompanied by a number of workers, and find a site in which to found a new nest. Thirdly, if she wanders off alone, she may enter a nest of a related but smaller species, the large black ant *Formica fusca,* displace the single queen and lay her own eggs, which are tended by the *fusca* workers. For a while there are both *fusca* and *rufa* workers in the nest, until the former die out, as there is no longer a *fusca* queen, and so a well-established wood ants' nest is founded.

Ant farms

Wood ants are fierce carnivores and bring great numbers of insects, especially caterpillars, back to the nest. Small victims are carried by single ants, large ones are dragged along by teams. The prey is devoured by the workers, who then feed the larvae from their mouths with liquid nourishment. Wood ants also tend and 'milk' aphids on trees and bushes, especially oak and birch. A tree supporting a large number of these aphids is treated as a 'farm' by the ants of a particular nest and is jealously guarded, and a column of ants can be seen running up and down its trunk. To obtain a meal of honeydew the ant solicits an aphid by stroking it with its antennae. The aphid responds by giving out a drop of its sugary excreta which the ant eagerly licks up. This sugar is the main energy-producing food of the ants, and a Swedish entomologist has calculated that the occupants of a single large wood ant nest may collect the equivalent of 20 lb of dry sugar in a season.

Chemical warfare

Wood ants are well armed for chemical warfare and their active enemies have been said to be limited to woodpeckers and man. When threatened the ant curls its abdomen forward between its legs and squirts a spray of formic acid at its enemy. In actual fighting it bites with its sharp jaws and then ejects acid into the bite. The strength of the formic acid can be tested by leaning closely over a nest and smelling the sharp tang of the acid or feeling it sting the eyes.

The green woodpecker disregards the biting and acid spray and may sometimes be seen head-down and half buried in a nest, licking up the outraged inhabitants with its long sticky tongue.

At one time wood ants' nests were regularly raided by animal dealers for the 'ants' eggs', which were sold to feed cage birds and aquarium fish. As long ago as 1880 the German forestry authorities, recognising the great service that these ants do in destroying insect pests among the trees, had a law passed forbidding interference with the nests under penalty of a fine or imprisonment. Today, pet shop dealers are less energetic in collecting ant eggs and there are also fewer woodpeckers, but already there is a noticeable decline in the number of wood ant nests, for the ant now has a far more dangerous enemy: the bulldozer, which destroys the woods and heaths on which it lives.

phylum	**Arthropoda**
class	**Insecta**
order	**Hymenoptera**
family	**Formicidae**
genus & species	***Formica pratensis*** *meadow ant* ***F. rufa*** *common wood ant*

Below: this neat mound of dry stalks, twigs and pine needles is the product of much hard labour by thousands of common wood ants. The workers (above) are constantly collecting more thatch material, so that the nest mound may reach several feet in height and, as here, it is often constructed at the base of a tree. Underneath, snug and dry, are the galleries and chambers of the nest proper, connected to the exterior by channels closed at night.

Woodchuck

The woodchuck, also known as a whistle-pig and popularly called a 'chuck', is a common rodent with a reputation for forecasting the weather in most of Canada and the eastern United States. Its body is thickset and 18—27 in. long. It has a 6in. hairy tail. Its weight varies from a little over 5 lb when the animal emerges from hibernation in the spring to 10 lb in September. The largest woodchucks may weigh as much as 14 lb at this time. The head is flattened with small ears, and the four toes have long claws used for digging. The colour of the fur varies from yellow to reddish-brown.

The woodchuck's range extends from Labrador and Nova Scotia, south to Virginia and Alabama, west to Kansas and north through Minnesota and Central Canada to the northern Rocky Mountains.

True hibernation

The woodchuck frequents woods and farm-land and digs its burrow on a rocky hillside or in a gully, but preferably in bushy woods at the edge of meadowland. The burrow has several exits and the entrance has a large pile of freshly removed earth around it. The burrows vary in depth according to the soil; in soft earth a tunnel may be as much as 6½ ft below the surface. The burrow consists of several compartments for sleeping, hibernating and for toilets. The toilets are cleaned regularly and the waste taken up and buried in the entrance mound. The woodchuck is solitary and diurnal, feeding in the morning and again in late afternoon or evening. It never wanders far from its burrow, its home range being only about 100 yd. It can swim well and unlike most large rodents will climb for food.

In autumn the woodchuck hibernates, starting earlier in the northern parts of its range. It settles down in one of the chambers in its burrow, sealing it off with earth. It then rolls up in a ball and goes into a deep sleep. Its breathing slows down until it almost stops: 14 breaths per minute against the normal of 262. Its temperature gradually drops to 4—14°C/40—57°F, as against the normal of 37—40°C/94.8—104°F. When the woodchuck emerges in the spring it looks very thin and hungry and has lost as much as half its weight.

A pest to farm crops

The woodchuck is mainly vegetarian, feeding on grass, leaves and flowers, particularly clover, and sometimes acorns. It will eat bark from trees and also takes fruits such as blackberries, raspberries, cherries and windfall apples. It will occasionally eat snails, insects and small birds. In some farm-land areas the woodchuck has become a pest, eating all kinds of farm produce and cereal crops. In addition to feeding voraciously it spoils the crops by trampling, and in some parts of the United States the wood-chuck's numbers have had to be controlled by gassing it in its burrow.

▷ *Favourite stance for a curious woodchuck.*

Leonard Lee Rue: Photo Res

Looking for a mate

As soon as the male woodchuck comes out of hibernation in the spring it goes to look for a mate. Fights often break out between two males and considerable damage may be inflicted before the weaker animal retreats, leaving the victor in possession of the female. Mating takes place in March and April and, after a gestation period of 28–32 days, 2–8, on average 4, babies are born in the burrow. The young 'chuck is pink, naked and blind, less than 4 in. long and weighing only 1–1½ oz. The female feeds her babies sitting on her haunches or standing on all fours. At the end of a month the youngsters' eyes open and they make their first trip out of the burrow. They are weaned in 35 days, and by midsummer have been driven out of the home burrow but continue to live in one nearby. The mother still watches over the youngsters and at the first sign of danger warns them with an alarm whistle. The young are sexually mature at one year.

Many enemies

The woodchuck has many natural enemies. It is preyed upon by bears, coyotes, wolves, mountain lions, as well as by eagles and hawks, and is often attacked by farm dogs. In addition, man hunts it for sport and for its flesh which, except when old, makes very good eating. The hunters, however, have to be very quick and sharp-eyed as 'chucks are very wary and bolt for cover at the slightest hint of danger.

Weather forecaster

The woodchuck is a legendary weather forecaster in America. It is said that if it emerges from hibernation on Candlemas Day, February 2nd, and sees its shadow, it returns to sleep for another six weeks and there will be another six weeks of winter. If, however, it does not see its shadow then winter is over and spring has come. According to Will Barker, in *Familiar Animals of America*, this legend dates back to early Colonial times. He states that in European folklore it was the badger that was supposed to look for its shadow on Candlemas Day, and early European settlers in America transferred the myth to the woodchuck. It is, however, hard to find confirmation of this belief regarding the badger.

class	**Mammalia**
order	**Rodentia**
family	**Sciuridae**
genus & species	***Marmota monax***

◁ *A young woodchuck on a cautious outing from the safety of mother's burrow. When the 4 young, born in spring, are a month old their eyes open and they take their first tentative steps outside. They are weaned at 35 days and are driven from the burrow by the mother within a month or two. The young woodchuck take up residence nearby where she can keep an eye on them and warn them when danger threatens.*

William Vandivert

Woodcock

Woodcock belong to the sandpiper family and are most closely related to snipe (p 2190). They are larger than snipe, about 13 in. long, with brown plumage mottled and barred with black. The bill is straight and 3 in. long and the eye is set well back on the head giving the woodcock a distinctive expression. The eye socket is very large and the opening of the ear lies below the socket rather than behind it. Compared with the snipe the head is large, the neck short and the wings are rounded.

There are two species of woodcock. The Eurasian woodcock breeds in much of Europe, including the British Isles, except the extreme north and south, and across Asia to Japan. It is also found in the Azores, Canaries and Madeira, Asia Minor, the Himalayas, Indonesia and New Guinea, though in the latter two regions it may be a related species. Its plumage is very like an owl's and makes a perfect camouflage among dead leaves. The back and wings are dark brown, mottled with black and buff and the crown of the head is dark with light transverse bars. The underparts are light brown with dark brown bars. The American woodcock is confined to the eastern half of North America as far north as the Great Lakes and the St Lawrence. It is lighter in colour than the Eurasian woodcock and is buff underneath with no barring.

▽ Roding flight: each evening at sunset a male European woodcock wings his way in slow ritual flight around his territory.

Regular habits

Unlike most waders woodcock are solitary and it is most unusual to see more than two together. They live in coniferous and deciduous woodlands, especially where there is bramble or some other type of undergrowth. More open ground, such as heaths with scattered trees or the edges of moors, is also frequented and there is a preference for damp places such as wet hollows in woodlands and marshy areas.

During the day woodcock lie up in dry places, among bracken, heather or brambles. They sit very still, relying on their plumage to conceal them, only flying up when almost stepped on. Then they rise swiftly with a great whirr of wings, which has been described as sounding like the ripping of stiff paper. The flight is strong and rapid as the woodcock manoeuvres between the trees, but it soon settles again. Feeding and courtship flights take place at dawn and dusk. Woodcock fly just above the treetops or along woodland rides and with their unmistakable outline it is easy to identify them as they make their regular flights along the same route each evening.

In the British Isles most woodcock are sedentary but in the northern parts of their range they regularly migrate southwards in winter, into North Africa and southern Asia. The American woodcock migrates into the southern United States.

Nimble bills

The food of woodcock is largely earthworms; a diet of 86% earthworms has been reported for the American woodcock. They also eat ground-living insects and their larvae, including earwigs, caterpillars and beetles. Centipedes and spiders are also eaten and occasionally freshwater molluscs. Woodcock usually feed at twilight, on damp ground, but in bad weather they may forage in leaf litter and along the shore.

Earthworms and other animals are sought by probing the soil with the long bill. The tip of the bill is well supplied with nerves and it is thought that the woodcock locates its food by touch. The bill is thrust into the soil with the mandibles closed but the tip of each mandible can be twisted outwards to seize an earthworm or other animal so the whole bill does not have to be forced open against the pressure of the earth. Thus earthworms can be swallowed without the bill being withdrawn from the soil.

The roding of woodcock

At dusk and dawn during the breeding season male woodcock make special flights around their territories. In Britain this flight is known as 'roding'. The woodcock flies at about 20–30 ft with slow, owl-like wingbeats and follows a regular course for up to an hour, starting at sunset. Two sounds can be heard as a roding woodcock flies past. One is a thin, far-carrying whistle, the other a low croak which is heard as the woodcock checks in its flight. It has been suggested that the croak is made by air rushing past three, narrow, stiff primary flight feathers but there is also evidence that this is a vocal sound. When two roding males meet they chase each other and females are also chased. Clearly, roding has the function of song in proclaiming ownership of a territory. The male courts the female by strutting around her with his feathers fluffed out and wings drooping.

Although his plumage is as well camouflaged as the female's the male woodcock takes no part in incubation and rearing his chicks. After mating the female makes a depression in the ground, lined with leaves and usually at the foot of a tree. She lays 3 or 4 well camouflaged eggs and incubates them for 20–21 days. The chicks fly in three weeks and there may be two broods in a season. If the brood is disturbed the adult 'feigns injury' by flying with tail spread and legs lowered or else it runs about with the tail fanned and the wings drooped or thrashing.

Rides for babies

Woodcock are among the few birds that carry their young. Jacanas (p 1173) carry their chicks under their wings and swans carry their broods on their backs. Both the American and Eurasian woodcock have been reported to carry chicks but, not surprisingly, reliable evidence is not easy to obtain because of the difficulty of being certain that a woodcock is carrying something as it speeds away. In a survey carried out in Britain 142 cases of carrying chicks were reported, and in 97 of them the chicks were carried between the legs. The rest were carried between the feet or on the back. Occasionally a woodcock has been seen to return and pick up another chick until the whole brood has been removed.

class	**Aves**
order	**Charadriiformes**
family	**Scolopacidae**
genera & species	***Scolopax rusticola*** *Eurasian woodcock* ***Philohela minor*** *American woodcock*

▽ *Sitting tight on her eggs a female woodcock will lie low until almost trodden on.*

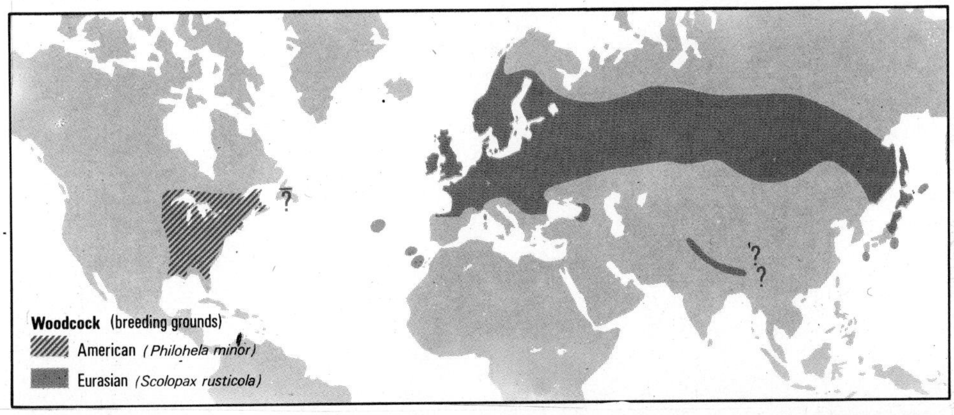

D Middleton: Photo Res

*Its beak adapted as a probe, the strong-billed woodcreeper **Xiphocolaptes promeropirhynchus**.*

Constance P Warner

Woodcreeper

The woodcreepers or woodhewers are fairly small, slender-bodied, dull coloured birds related to the ovenbirds. They are 5 – 18 in. long and they look rather like creepers (p 566), the resemblance being due to convergent evolution as the two groups of birds have similar habits. Both climb agilely on tree trunks and the woodcreepers have sharp, curved claws and stiff, woodpecker-like tail feathers for gripping vertical trunks.

There are about 50 species of wood-creepers, many being difficult to distinguish in the field because of the uniformity of their drab plumage and the difficulty of observing them among foliage. The plumage is mainly dull brown with reddish wings and tail and light stripes on the head, nape and underparts. There is considerable variation in the size and shape of the bill. It is usually stout, sometimes flattened and chisel-like or down-curved. The most extreme bill is found in the scythebill or sicklebill, which has a 3in. down-curved bill making up about a third of the total length of the bird. The barred woodcreeper has an almost straight bill with a hook at the tip, the
allied woodhewer has a slender pointed bill.

Woodcreepers live in tropical America, from Sonora in north-west Mexico to northern Argentina, and in Trinidad and Tobago.

Solitary with simple songs

Woodcreepers are woodland and forest birds. They are solitary and little is known of the habits of most species. None migrate, with the possible exception of the narrow-billed woodcreeper, and they have poor songs consisting of repetitive trills, whistles and harsh notes. The allied woodhewer lives in forests where the trees are covered in mosses and epiphytic flowers but it also comes into clearings where there are only scattered trees. Like most other woodcreepers it can be seen hopping up and around tree-trunks then flying to another tree and repeating the process. A few woodcreepers, however, feed on the ground, such as the great rufous woodcreeper of Argentina.

Probing for food

The bill is not used as a chisel, like the woodpecker's, but as a probe, like the creeper's, for searching in crevices in bark or among the plants growing on the tree trunks. Grubs are pulled out of their burrows and loose bark is sometimes prised off to reveal other animals. In addition to
insects and their larvae, spiders, small snails and frogs are also eaten.

Borrowed nests

As far as is known woodcreepers nest in cavities in trees, from ground level up to about 30 ft, sometimes in earth banks or fallen logs or between the leaves of epiphytes. They are unable to excavate their own holes but use natural holes or those of barbets and woodpeckers, particularly if they are well concealed by moss and have narrow entrances. Sometimes no material is added to form a nest but at other times pieces of wood and bark from dead trees are deposited in the nest hole, particularly if it is very deep. There is one record of a buff-throated woodcreeper carrying some 7 000 pieces of material to its nest. They add material throughout the incubation period.

The clutch is of 2, sometimes 3, glossy white eggs. The incubation period of the streak-headed woodcreeper is 15 days and in the allied woodhewer the chicks spend 19 days in the nest. Both parents care for the brood, incubating the eggs then brooding and feeding the chicks, which are fed for a few weeks after they leave the nest.

Second-class diner

The range of the woodcreepers is very similar to that of the antbirds and both have the habit of following advancing hordes of army ants (p 87), feeding on the small animals that they flush. The plain-brown woodcreeper, for instance, flies from perch to perch just above the army ants and swoops out to catch the fleeing animals. In some parts of its range it comes into conflict with the ocellated ant-thrush which has similar habits and drives the woodcreeper from the lower levels of the undergrowth, where it is easier to catch fugitives from the army ants. As an ant-thrush approaches, the woodcreeper hops up the tree, returning once the ant-thrush has passed. The woodcreepers also have to keep to the edges of the ant swarm whereas the ant-thrushes can forage in the centre. Such competition between unrelated species will only have an adverse effect on the dominated species if there is a shortage of food. It appears, however, that the ants flush so many animals that the woodcreepers can find sufficient food even when driven from the best pitches.

class	Aves
order	Passeriformes
family	Dendrocolaptidae
genera & species	*Campylorhamphus falcularius* scythebill
	Dendrocolaptes certhia barred
	Dendrocincla fuliginosa plain-brown
	Lepidocolaptes affinis allied woodhewer
	L. angustirostris narrow-billed
	L. souleyetii streak-headed
	Xiphocolaptes major great rufous
	Xiphorhynchus guttatus buff-throated
	others

Wood duck

The wood or Carolina duck, sometimes called the tree duck, is one of the most ornately-plumaged ducks, probably attaining second place after its close relative, the mandarin duck. It is 20 in. long, rather smaller than an eider, with a large head, short neck and a long square tail. The bill is short and the toes bear sharp claws. The breeding plumage of the male almost defies description; the feathers of the back have metallic, iridescent colours, mainly green with blue on the trailing edges of the wings. The upper breast is reddish-brown and the flanks orange-brown with white margins. The belly is whitish. The head bears a trailing crest, purple and green with white markings. The eye is red and the bill mainly white with red and yellow at the base. In its eclipse plumage the male resembles the female but has more white under the chin. The female has a small crest and is mainly grey above with blue on the wings, and brown with white spots underneath.

The wood duck is confined to the United States and the southern parts of Canada. Its close relative, the mandarin duck, lives in eastern Asia and Japan and has almost identical habits. Its plumage is even more gaudy than that of the wood duck, having a larger crest and upswept 'fins' on the back. The females of the two species are, however, virtually indistinguishable. Despite their close relationship the two species never interbreed. Indeed, the mandarin does not interbreed with any species, although the wood duck has bred in captivity with several species of **Anas** ducks.

The maned goose or wood duck of Australia belongs to the same group of perching ducks as the wood duck of North America. It is found over most of Australia and often nests in trees.

▽ Celebrated aristocrat, the Carolina duck.

◁ *Like its close relative the Carolina duck, the mandarin duck is a familiar sight on ornamental ponds, but its real home is China, where pairs were formerly given as wedding presents to symbolise marital fidelity.*

◁▽ *A graceful pair of wood duck at home. These birds were once brought to the verge of extinction in the wild by indiscriminate hunting, but numbers are now recovering.*

▷ *A harassed wood duck sees an intruder off the premises. In her nest in a hollow tree she will be kept busy incubating a clutch of 6–15 eggs with no help from her mate.*

branch has broken off or in the abandoned nests of woodpeckers, flickers and fox squirrels. The ducks are able to squeeze through surprisingly small holes. The hole may be as much as 50 ft up or as low as 5 ft and is usually near water, but if there are no suitable sites, the ducks may be forced to nest a mile from the nearest stretch of water. In these circumstances there is often competition with the hooded merganser which sometimes results in a duck of each species laying eggs in one nest hole.

Apart from the remains of the previous tenant's nest, the nest consists of only a layer of down plucked from the duck's breast. The clutch consists of 6–15 eggs which are incubated for 28–30 days by the female while the male waits nearby. Although there are descriptions of newly hatched wood ducks being carried down from the nest by the mother, it is usual for them to jump down, encouraged by her calls. Shortly after they are hatched, the chicks scramble up the sides of the nest hole with the aid of their sharp claws and drop to the ground. The parents then escort them to the water.

Help for the wood duck

At one time the wood duck was one of the most widespread and commonest ducks in the United States but by the early years of the 20th century its numbers had been so reduced that there were fears for its survival in the wild. Although a fast and agile flier it had been shot in vast numbers, while the clearing of trees, especially of dead trees, robbed it of nesting places. Luckily the wood duck, like the mandarin, was highly prized by aviculturalists and by the First World War there were probably more wood duck in captivity than in the wild. At this point Alain White set up a sanctuary to breed wood duck. By 1939, when the project was ended, more than 9 000 wood duck had been successfully reared and then released to spread either locally or in other states.

An individual duck

The wood duck is sometimes called the summer duck because it nests in the southern states whereas other ducks merely stay for the winter, migrating north in spring for nesting. The wood duck has only a limited migration, a few individuals staying in the northern part of the range for the winter and a few migrating south of the United States. Migrating wood duck travel in small parties, not mixing with other ducks. Their only calls are whistles.

The wood duck is exclusively a freshwater duck, living on ponds, streams and swampy woodland. It roosts on small ponds and flies out in the early morning to its feeding grounds. Unlike many ducks it is extremely agile in the air and darts through thick forests with remarkable ease, turning and dodging between branches, even at dusk. Wood ducks walk well and climb agilely along branches.

Surface feeder

Wood duck feed mainly on plants floating on the surface or growing just above the water, although they do upend in shallow water to feed on the bottom. The seeds and leaves of many water plants are taken, including those of grasses, docks, wild celery and wild rice, and underwater bulbs and tubers are uprooted. Wood duck also forage for acorns and chestnuts on the forest floor. In the summer a considerable proportion of the diet is made up of animal food taken from around the surface of the water. Two thirds of this is insects, such as beetles, dragonflies and damselflies and their larvae, and the rest is snails, crustaceans, small amphibians, and small fish such as minnows.

Sharing nests

Apart from occasional nests in rock crevices, wood duck always nest in holes in trees, either natural cavities formed where a

class	**Aves**
order	**Anseriformes**
family	**Anatidae**
genera & species	***Aix galericulata*** mandarin duck **_A. sponsa_** wood duck ***Chenonetta jubata*** maned goose

Woodlouse

Woodlice, or sow-bugs as they are called in America, are particularly interesting as they are the only crustaceans that have become completely adapted to spending their whole life on land. They are small, never reaching more than ¾ in. long, with oval bodies, convex above and flat or hollow beneath. The head and abdomen are small but the thorax is comparatively large, composed of seven hard, individual overlapping plates. There are seven pairs of legs, the last pair appearing only after the first moult.

Two of the commonest European woodlice are **Oniscus asellus** which has a brownish body and two rows of yellowish spots on the back and **Porcellio scaber** which is bluish-grey. These two are rather flat and do not roll up into a ball when touched. The pill woodlouse, **Armadillidium vulgare,** on the other hand, has a more convex dorsal surface and readily rolls up into a ball when handled, which makes it look like a small grey pill — indeed it was formerly used as a popular medicine. A small, blind, colourless woodlouse, **Platyarthrus hoffmannseggi** is occasionally found in the nests of ants in southern England. In fact it is never found apart from ants, who seem to tolerate its presence without aggression.

Woodlice are found in all temperate and tropical parts of the world.

Damp, dark places necessary

All woodlice are scavengers, hiding by day in dark, damp places under bark, stones, piles of leaves or in cracks in the ground, and only coming out into the open at night. Dampness is essential to the woodlouse and in dry air it will die in about 2 hours. It is noticeable that a woodlouse walks much more quickly in dry places and slows down in damp situations. Similarly it tends to aggregate with other woodlice when the air is dry probably because, when bunched together, they lose water much less rapidly, so their chances of survival increase. The pill woodlouse is much more resistant to drying up and can often be seen walking about in strong sunlight.

About nine or ten times in its life a woodlouse retires into a quiet, sheltered corner to moult its shell and grow a new one. This is necessary as the shell is rigid and does not grow with the animal. The rear segments of its shell fall off first and after about three days the front segments are moulted. This leaves the woodlouse more or less defenceless — vulnerable even to members of its own kind which will eat it without any hesitation.

Heather Angel

Series by Heinz Schrempp

How they breathe

If the underside of a woodlouse such as *Porcellio scaber* is examined with a lens, a white spot can be seen on the outer plates of each of the first two pairs of abdominal appendages. These white spots are the tufts of fine branching tubes in the interior of the appendages. The tubes are filled with air and open to the outside by a minute pore. They represent, in fact, the beginnings of a tracheal system like the respiratory systems of insects and certain other air-breathing arthropods. It is impossible to suppose, however, that woodlice are in any way closely related to insects, and their tracheae must have evolved independently from those of insects.

Small but independent

The breeding habits of *Porcellio scaber* have been observed but little is known about the habits of other species. After fertilisation by the male a brood pouch appears as a white

Above: Grouped on the underside of bark, adult and young **Porcellio scaber** *and (bottom right)* **Oniscus asellus**.
Right: When disturbed a pill woodlouse rolls itself up into an armour-plated ball. The thick carapace prevents water loss from the body and serves as protection against predators. The antennae are the first to show as the woodlouse uncurls, in this case it lies on its back, flailing its legs to right itself. Finally—ready for action.

triangular patch between the female's fore-legs. About 20 or more eggs are laid in the pouch, which becomes slightly distended. The pouch is transparent, so the eggs can be seen clearly through a hand lens. They grow larger and larger until they burst and the embryo young emerge. About 6 weeks after fertilisation a split appears in the pouch through which the young escape, one at a time, over a period of 2 or 3 days. Although only about $\frac{1}{16}$ in. long they are pearly white with large black eye spots and six pairs of stumpy legs. They are completely independent. After all the young have emerged the brood pouch becomes flat again and is sloughed off at the next moult, when a new one grows.

Repelling spiders

Spiders are the most serious enemies of woodlice, which defend themselves by secretions from their lobed glands that make them distasteful. These secretions are also used by *Platyarthrus hoffmannseggi* to repel ants, centipedes and other predators.

Dry society

Although woodlice look like insects there are many differences between them. For example, in the outer layers of an insect cuticle is a wax which prevents evaporation of moisture. Insects also have other ways of conserving water, such as eliminating dry faeces. Woodlice have none of these and readily lose moisture in a dry atmosphere. They are therefore very dependent on moisture and they have special sense-organs in the tough outer skin for detecting it. Woodlice also have an urge to move away from light, but if one is in a dark place that dries out it will tend to move towards the light. Therefore, if a woodlouse is in a moist, dark place it stays there, but in a dry, light situation it is compelled to wander, until it reaches a dark, damp place. When woodlice bunch together they reduce the amount of evaporation from their bodies, and when one woodlouse smells another it automatically walks towards it. This is what brings them together in a bunch. There is, however, an exception to this. When a woodlouse has been kept for a day in moist surroundings it is more likely than not to be quite unmoved by the odour of its fellow woodlice. Finally, since a woodlouse is so attracted to dark damp places what makes it come out at night to feed? When it has been in the dark for 10 hours or more it becomes restless and must wander.

phylum	**Arthropoda**
class	**Crustacea**
order	**Isopoda**
genera	***Armadillidium, Kogmania, Ligia, Oniscus, Platyarthrus, Porcellio, Schoblia, Trichoniscus, Tylos***

Top: **Platyarthrus hoffmannseggi** *with its newly born young. They shed their skins immediately after birth making their first meal of them. Centre and bottom: An adult of the same species also sheds its skin and eats it.*

Woodpecker

No birds are better adapted for a life on the branches and trunks of trees than the woodpeckers. Two of the true woodpeckers are described under the separate headings of flicker (p 783) and sapsucker (p 2023). There are about 200 species of true woodpecker which are spread over the wooded parts of the world, except Madagascar, Australia and oceanic islands. They are up to nearly 2 ft long and are usually brightly-coloured with patterns of black, white, green or red. A few woodpeckers have crests. The bill is straight and pointed, the legs short with two toes facing backwards and the tail is made up of pointed feathers with stiff shafts.

The 15 species of green woodpeckers inhabit the woods and forests of Europe and Asia from the British Isles to Borneo and Java. The familiar green woodpecker of Europe is 12 in. long, and has a green plumage, which is brighter below, a bright yellowish rump and a red crown. The male has a red and black stripe under the eye, while the female has a plain black stripe. The pied or spotted woodpeckers form a widespread group, the 30-odd species being distributed across North America, Europe and Asia. They are black or grey with white patches, bars or mottling. The males often have red crowns. The three-toed woodpeckers are unusual in having one toe missing from each foot. They too have a circumpolar distribution. The ivorybills of America are the largest woodpeckers and inhabit forests of large trees. As a result of these forests being cut down these species are in danger of extinction. The ivory-billed woodpecker of North America and Cuba was thought to be extinct but in 1966 a few pairs were found in Texas.

Expert tree climbers

Woodpeckers are usually seen as just a flash of colour disappearing through the trees. They live solitarily in woods and can be identified by their characteristic undulating flight: 3—4 rapid wingbeats carrying them up, followed by a downward glide. They are more likely to be given away by their harsh or ringing calls, such as the loud laugh of the green woodpecker, or by their drumming, a rapid tattoo which they make with their bills on dead branches, or even on metal roofs.

Woodpeckers spend most of their time hopping up tree trunks in spirals, searching for insects. When a woodpecker has searched one tree it flies to the base of the next and repeats the operation. In climbing vertical trunks, woodpeckers are assisted by having two backward-facing toes, sharp claws, and stiff tail feathers, which are used as a prop while climbing, rather like a shooting stick.

Which nest hole is the best hole? Upper: Female African **Campethera abingoni.** *Below: Great spotted woodpecker* **Dendrocopos major.**

Peter Johnson

Albert Visage : Jacana

Boring for insects

The woodpecker's food is largely insects and their larvae. The green woodpeckers often hunt on the ground for ants and sometimes attack bee hives. The red-headed woodpecker of North America catches insects on the wing. Otherwise woodpeckers feed on insects which are prised out of crevices in the bark or drilled out of the wood. The pointed bill is an excellent chisel and the skull is toughened to withstand the shock of hammering. When drilling, a woodpecker aims its blows alternately from one side then the other, like a woodman felling a tree. Insects are removed from the hole by using the woodpecker's second useful tool—an extremely long tongue; it can protrude up to 6 in. from the tip of the bill in the green woodpecker. The tongue is protruded by the same mechanism as that of the piculet (p 1749). It is often tipped with barbs or bristles or coated with mucus for brushing up the insects.

Some woodpeckers eat fruit and seeds or drink sap. Red-headed woodpeckers and acorn woodpeckers store acorns, drilling separate holes in trees for each acorn or else using a natural cavity. There is a story of an acorn woodpecker that spent an autumn feeding acorns into a knothole in the wall of a cabin. As the hole never filled, the woodpecker 'posted' several hundred acorns in it.

Nesting in holes

With the exception of the African ground woodpecker, which burrows in the ground, woodpeckers nest in holes that they excavate in trees. They drill into a trunk then tunnel downwards to make a cavity up to 1 ft deep. There is no nest lining and the 2–8 white eggs rest on the bottom of the cavity. The eggs hatch in 11–17 days and the chicks fledge in 2–3 weeks, depending on the size of the woodpecker. Both sexes bore the nest hole, and takes turns at incubating and feeding the chicks.

Evacuating the home

Boring a nest hole several inches across does considerable damage to a tree and may weaken it sufficiently for it to fall. This happened at a nest of a pileated woodpecker observed by FK Truslow in the Everglades National Park. The tree split off at the level of the entrance to the nest, revealing that the trunk had been hollowed to leave a shell only $\frac{1}{4}$–$\frac{1}{2}$ in. thick. Truslow stayed in his hide hoping to watch the reactions of the woodpeckers—the female was incubating at the time. About 10 minutes later the female woodpecker did a most remarkable thing. She returned to the tree, disappeared into the nest cavity and reappeared with an egg in her bill. She then flew off with it and did not drop it for the 75 yd she was in sight. All three eggs were removed in this manner. Unfortunately this extraordinary story has no satisfactory ending as he never found out what became of the eggs. It is, however, one of the few positive records we have of birds rescuing their eggs by carrying them away.

Peter J Green

class	**Aves**
order	**Piciformes**
family	**Picidae**
genera	***Campephilus principalis***
& species	*ivory-billed woodpecker*
	Dendrocopos major
	great spotted woodpecker
	D. minor
	lesser spotted woodpecker
	Dryocopus pileatus
	pileated woodpecker
	Geocolaptes olivaceus
	ground woodpecker
	Melanerpes erythrocephalus
	red-headed woodpecker
	M. formicivorus
	acorn woodpecker
	Picoides tridactylus
	three-toed woodpecker
	Picus viridis
	green woodpecker

◁ *Rare photograph of a pair of ivory-billed woodpeckers. The former distribution of this striking bird was the once heavily wooded bottomlands of the Mississippi basin. With the felling of giant cypresses, water oaks and black gums, the birds' habitat was destroyed. Today a few pairs live in the near-virgin forests of Texas and Louisiana—their last refuge.*
▷ *In complete contrast: the lesser spotted woodpecker is widespread in the woods of Europe; but, although numerous, it is seldom seen.*

△ *Just beginning to lose their sparse yellow down, a pair of large young wood pigeons wait for the arrival of one or other of their parents with some food. After their first three days, when they are fed with pigeon's milk, their main diet is ripe cereal grain.*

▷ *Two greedy young wood pigeons eagerly reach out of the nest trying to get more food from their ever-patient parent. They remain in the nest for about 22 days, but for at least another week afterwards they are fed by one or both parents.*

▽ *One of the greatest enemies of farmers in Europe, the gentle-looking wood pigeon is easily distinguishable from other doves by the white patch on the sides of its neck. In order to reduce their numbers, the most effective method has proved to be nest destruction.*

Wood pigeon

From being a harmless rarity up to the end of the 18th century, the wood pigeon, or ring dove, has become one of the most common and most destructive pests of agricultural land, especially in certain parts of Europe. It is a handsome, rather heavily built bird, about 16 in. long with a wing span of about 18 in. The upper parts are bluish-grey with darker grey on the upper wings and black on the upper tail and wing quills. The breast is vinous shading to pale grey or lavender on the belly, flanks and under the tail. The rump and head are a bluer grey than the rest and the sides of the neck are a metallic purple and green. The base of the bill is pink, the rest yellow shading to pale brown on the tip. The base of the bill expands into a soft fleshy lump over the nostrils. The legs and feet are pink with a mauve tinge. The straw colour of the eye and its unusual pear-shaped iris give the bird a very alert expression. The wood pigeon can always be distinguished from other doves by the white patch on the sides of the neck, which is absent in young birds, and the broad white band across the wing. The male and female are alike except that the males tend to be slightly larger and their plumage brighter.

The typical race of the wood pigeon is found throughout Europe, except in the extreme north. It ranges eastwards to Russia and in the south extends to the north coast of the Mediterranean and to the various Mediterranean islands from the Balearics to Cyprus, and around the Black Sea. It is replaced by allied races in northwest Africa, the Azores, Madeira, Turkestan and Transcaspia to Persia, Baluchistan, Kashmir and Sikkim.

Wary in the country

The wood pigeon is primarily a bird of the woods but since the spread of agriculture it has taken to feeding on cultivated land. It is also a familiar bird in town parks and suburban gardens and is often found on downs and on coasts, some way from woods.

Albert Visage: Jacana

Wood pigeon *(Columba palumbus)* Breeding grounds

From autumn to spring and sometimes also in summer it congregates in large flocks to feed, although single birds and small groups may also be seen. In the towns and parks it may become quite tame but in the open country it is wary of humans and will take off with a loud clatter of wings at the slightest disturbance. Its normal flight is fast and strong with quick regular wing-beats and occasional glides. On the ground it struts about, restlessly moving its head to and fro. It roosts in trees, sometimes in large numbers.

The wood pigeon's voice, which is heard at all times of the year but more frequently in March and April, is often said to be a series of coos but the phrase 'two coos, Taffy take' repeated several times gives a better idea. The alarm note is a short, sharp 'roo' sound.

Agricultural menace

Originally the wood pigeon fed on acorns and beech mast as well as seeds, nuts, berries and the young leaves of many trees. Since the spread of agriculture and the disappearance of many woods it has turned, to a large extent, in many areas to cultivated crops and found them just as palatable and in greater abundance. Cereal grains are the most important food for both adults and young in late summer and autumn and in some areas peas and beans are taken in large quantities. In winter the birds depend mainly on clover, turnip tops and young greens. The pronounced hook at the end of the bill makes it easy for the pigeon to tear off the leaves of these plants. Some animal food is taken including caterpillars, earthworms, slugs, snails and insects.

The wood pigeon needs quite a large quantity of water and drinks greedily, not in sips like most other birds.

Billing and cooing

The courtship of a pair of wood pigeons begins while they are still in flocks. A pair separate from the main body and on the ground or a perch in a tree they bow to each other, their breasts touching the ground or perch, with their tails raised and spread, all the time cooing to each other. This bowing and cooing is often interrupted by a nuptial display flight in which the bird rises steeply with strong wingbeats then glides down and rises again with stiff set

wings in an undulating course. At the top of its rising flight it usually makes several claps with its wings, caused by a strong downbeat of the wings and not, as so often supposed, by the wings clapping together. Also at this time pairs of birds start to establish territories in the trees, the males driving away any intruders with aggressive posturing or actual attacks.

Young fed on milk

The breeding season is long, usually from April to September, but there are records of nests in every month of the year for the southern parts of the wood pigeon's range. The peak of breeding activity seems to be July, August and September in the British Isles when there is plenty of ripe corn for feeding the young. There are usually three broods a year. The nest is built in almost any kind of tree or in tall hedgerows, sometimes on top of the old nest of crows or sparrowhawks or on a squirrel's drey. Very occasionally it is built close to the ground or on ledges of rocks. In towns, buildings are used. The nest is a flimsy structure of intertwined sticks, often used for several years in succession. The male brings the material but only the female builds. Usually two, occasionally one or three, white, fairly glossy eggs are laid and are incubated for about 18 days, by both parents.

When the young birds hatch they are covered in sparse yellow down and for the first three days are fed at frequent intervals on a fluid from the parents' crops known as 'pigeon's milk'. After this, ripe cereal grain is the main food with some green food and weed seeds supplemented with animal foods. They stay in the nest for about 22 days, and afterwards are still fed by one or both parents for at least another week.

The average age attained by a wood pigeon in the wild in the British Isles is only 38 months but the oldest one recorded was in its 14th year.

Large numbers shot

Apart from man the adult wood pigeon has few enemies, but many of their eggs are taken by jays and magpies. The losses among young birds are due mainly to starvation, especially when they leave the nests and compete for food with the adult birds. In really severe winters the mortality

among wood pigeons is very high but their numbers soon seem to increase again.

Owing to the widespread destruction of crops by wood pigeons a great deal of research has been done into methods of keeping down their numbers. Shooting the birds is still the most widely used method although some sportsmen contend that wood pigeons are difficult to shoot as the shot glances off their feathers. There is no evidence to show that widescale shooting makes any impression on their numbers.

Migrant or not?

The subject of migration of wood pigeons to and from the British Isles has provided a constant source of argument amongst countrymen, sportsmen and bird-watchers for many years. Apparently the wood pigeons in the British Isles are mainly sedentary but with a tendency to move south in the winter. Only a small proportion of the population undertakes long flights and these are usually young birds. There is probably a latent urge, inherited from migratory ancestors, which shows itself in only a few individuals. The only birds recovered abroad reached no farther than France. In continental Europe the migratory behaviour is rather different. Wood pigeons in Scandinavia and the Baltic are forced to migrate south in winter to escape the snow and some of these do arrive on the east coast of Britain, but the numbers vary considerably from year to year. Observers have told of hordes of wood pigeons arriving from the Continent and although large numbers may arrive in some years, confusion very often arises because of the flocks of wood pigeons that seem to fly out to sea from the British Isles and then fly back again!

class	**Aves**
order	**Columbiformes**
family	**Columbidae**
genus & species	*Columba palumbus*

2649

Constance P Warner

Loke Wan Tho: WWF

Loke Wan Tho: WWF

Wood-swallow

The wood-swallows, or swallow-shrikes, are an unusual group of birds. They are superficially like the swallows, but resemble miniature vultures in their habit of soaring. There are about 10 species of wood-swallow making up a family which is not related to the true swallows. They are 5–8 in. long, with stout bodies, long pointed wings and short tails. The plumage is soft and wood-swallows are the only songbirds with powder-down feathers which break up into powder for cleaning the plumage. Other birds with powder-down include the herons, parrots, and tinamous. The legs are short and strong and the bill stout and curved.

The white-breasted wood-swallow of southeast Asia and Australia is dark brown above with a white bar on the rump. The underparts are white except for a dark brown throat and upper breast. The bill

is blue with a black tip. The masked wood-swallow is grey above and greyish-white underneath. The face and throat are black with a white border. The smallest wood-swallow is the little wood-swallow, also of Australia, which is sooty-brown with black wings and black tail with a white tip.

Six of the ten wood-swallows live in Australia but others range from India, where the ashy swallow-shrike is found, to Fiji, with its white-breasted species.

Dense huddles

Despite their name, wood-swallows are found not in forests but in open country where they are easily recognised as they soar in flocks, emitting loud, harsh twittering calls. Apart from ravens and choughs, wood-swallows are the only passerine or perching birds that habitually glide or soar for extended periods. They soar in thermals like vultures (p 2542), sometimes climbing so high that they are lost to sight.

Another unusual feature of the wood-

swallows' habits is their extreme gregariousness. The flock usually forages from a particular vantage point such as a tree or, when possible, telephone wires. Unlike true swallows, which perch neatly spaced out, wood-swallows huddle together. Some species, such as the dusky wood-swallow, roost in clumps numbering up to 200, piled on top of each other, looking like a swarm of enormous bees.

Scourge of insects

Wood-swallows feed on insects, mainly flying ones, which they catch rather like fly-catchers. Individual wood-swallows fly out from the perch and snap up insects with their widely-opening bills and circle around for some time before returning to the perch. They feed mainly in the early morning and late evening. Wood-swallows are particularly beneficial to man because they descend in large flocks, sometimes of thousands, onto swarms of locusts and cutworms, the destructive caterpillars of owlet moths. The masked wood-swallow is sometimes a nuisance because it feeds on honey bees.

Father to the rescue

The nests of wood-swallows are usually very loosely constructed saucers of twigs, roots and grass. They are usually placed on a branch, among the bases of palm leaves or in a hole up to 50 ft above the ground. The little wood-swallow nests in colonies among rocks or on cave ledges and the white-rumped wood-swallow sometimes uses the solid nests of mudlarks, which it relines. The clutch is of 2—4 eggs and in the species for which information is available, incubation takes 12 days and is shared by the parents. The chicks fly in another 12 days. There is one record of a brood of young Papuan wood-swallows being fed by four or five adults. In such a gregarious bird this behaviour is not surprising and may be quite widespread.

There is also a remarkable story of two young white-browed wood-swallows fluttering to the ground and being rescued by the male parent who carried them, one at a time in his feet, to a branch. There is a report of a sand martin behaving in a similar manner in England.

Mean tricks

The rescue of the chicks is a remarkable story, but in *Bird Wonders of Australia* AH Chisholm recounts another anecdote that shows a meaner side to the wood-swallow's character. Chisholm was watching a newly-fledged cuckoo-shrike calling for food when a white-browed wood-swallow landed nearby. When the parent cuckoo-shrike appeared with food the wood-swallow swept past, grabbed the food from its bill and sped away with the cuckoo-shrike in pursuit. One must presume that the wood-swallow had somehow learned to associate the begging calls of the young cuckoo-shrike with the arrival of the parent bearing food in the bill. Thieving of this sort seems to be a very individual matter even in species which employ it fairly regularly, such as sheathbills (p 2109) and skuas (p 2160). In the article, Chisholm recounts how silver gulls in a particular part of Tasmania have formed the habit of riding on the backs of pelicans and grabbing the fish they catch.

◁ *Papuan wood-swallows nest on the top of a projecting stump or branch; parental duties are often shared—young birds have been seen being fed by four or five adults.*

△ *Masked wood-swallows congregate on a vine in a spacious captive enclosure. Wood-swallows are extremely sociable birds, they even roost in a compact huddle.*

class	**Aves**
order	**Passeriformes**
family	**Artamidae**
genus & species	*Artamus cyanopterus* dusky wood-swallow *A. fuscus* ashy swallow shrike *A. leucorhynchus* white-breasted wood-swallow *A. maximus* Papuan wood-swallow *A. minor* little wood-swallow *A. personatus* masked wood-swallow *A. superciliosus* white-browed wood-swallow others

*Well hidden in the woodland undergrowth, the wood-warbler **Phylloscopus sibilatrix** guards its young*

Wood-warbler

*The wood-warblers form a large family of small birds confined to the Americas. There are at present 113 species, but it has recently been suggested that the honeycreepers (p 1093) belong to the same family and differ only in their adaptations for drinking nectar. They range in size from 4 to 7 in. long and have narrow, straight bills. The plumage is sometimes dull grey or brown but in many species it is bright, usually yellow, orange or black and white. In tropical America both male and female are brightly coloured but in temperate latitudes the female is sombre and the male brightly coloured only in the breeding season. The large number of species makes identification difficult; the songs, call notes and the male plumage are the most diagnostic features. In Britain the wood-warbler **Phylloscopus sibilatrix** is a true warbler (p 2554).*

*A widespread wood-warbler is the yellow warbler **Dendroica petechia** in which the sexes are very similarly coloured: buff above, yellow underneath, yellow and black on the wings and tail, the male having rusty streaks on the breast. Many other wood-warblers have more right to the name 'yellow warbler', particularly the yellow-breasted chat **Icteria virens,** the largest wood-warbler, which is olive-green above and bright yellow below with white around the eyes. Kirtland's warbler **D. kirtlandii,** with a yellow breast and black-streaked flanks, is unusual in being confined to an area of 60 by 80 miles in Michigan, where there are dense growths of jack pines 3 – 18 ft high. Two wood-warblers have blue in the plumage; the black-throated blue warbler **D. caerulescens** is most striking with blue-grey upper parts, black cheeks and throat and white underparts. Two other*

*wood-warblers, the golden-winged – **Vermivora chysoptera** – and blue-winged – **V. pinus** – warblers, which are rather different in appearance, interbreed where their ranges overlap. The hybrids, which are fertile, were once considered separate species and were called Brewster's and Lawrence's warblers respectively.*

Wood-warblers breed from Alaska to southern South America, about half of which are found in North America and the West Indies. Like the vireos (p 2533), wood-warblers occasionally migrate across the Atlantic to Europe.

Impressive migrations

Wood-warblers are found mainly in woodland and scrub country but they have colonised a wide variety of habitats. The northern waterthrush lives in bogs and others are found in deserts and in tropical rain forests. The chestnut-sided warbler prefers scrub country and has benefited from the clearing of forests. Most northern wood-warblers are migratory, travelling in flocks to Central and northern South America, sometimes to Brazil and Chile. These flocks, in which several species of wood-warblers fly in company with tits, are one of the most spectacular sights of North American bird-watching. In the spring, migration is rapid, the blackpoll warbler taking a month to travel from Florida to Alaska, and 'waves' of warblers, many in brightly-coloured breeding plumage, pass through North America.

The songs of wood-warblers are simple when compared with the varied calls of Old World warblers but the yellow-breasted chat is a good mimic.

Mainly insect-eaters

Almost all wood-warblers eat insects and the majority feed among the foliage. The ovenbird and waterthrushes feed on the ground and some wood-warblers, like flycatchers, hawk for flying insects. The latter have flattened bills surrounded by bristles for sweeping up their prey. The black and white warbler searches for insects among

crevices in bark and has short legs and long claws which enable it to run up trunks like a creeper (p 566). It is able to stay north in the autumn after other wood-warblers have migrated because insects hiding in crevices survive longer than those in exposed places. As it eats fruit and berries, the myrtle warbler also survives colder weather and can live in areas where there is snow in winter.

Varied nest sites

The nests of wood-warblers are cup-shaped or domed, some being built 50 ft or more up in the tops of trees and others on the ground. The parula warbler builds its nests in hanging skeins of Spanish moss. The nest of the ovenbird, not to be confused with the ovenbirds of the family Furnariidae (p 1649), is a dome-shaped nest of leaves built on the ground. The prothonotary warbler sometimes builds in holes or nest boxes. It is named after the papal secretary who wears orange-yellow robes. In tropical America the clutch is 2 or 3 eggs but in temperate latitudes it is 3–5. The female alone incubates but both parents feed the chicks. Incubation ranges from 10 to 16 days and fledging from 8 to 14 days. The periods are shorter in tropical than in the northern migratory species.

Saving Kirtland's warbler

The story of Kirtland's warbler has been told by HF Mayfield in *The Kirtland's Warbler*. Its nesting place was discovered in Michigan in 1903 and it was later found that it wintered only in the Bahamas. It is not evenly distributed through the jack pine forests as it has a definite preference for young trees, moving into areas about 6 years after felling or burning when saplings have reached a height of 6 ft. There is now a programme of controlled burning to ensure that a suitable habitat is always available. In 1951 a painstaking census revealed 432 singing males and 10 years later 502 were found. This suggests a stable population of about 1 000 breeding pairs, a woefully small number to ensure survival. The warbler is, however, protected by law and, more important, by public sentiment in both its summer and its winter homes. Disaster could, however, befall it while migrating and its numbers seem to be severely limited by cowbirds which parasitise half the nests each year.

class	**Aves**
order	**Passeriformes**
family	**Parulidae**
genera & species	***Dendroica coronata*** *myrtle warbler*
	D. striata *blackpoll warbler*
	Geothlypis trichas *yellowthroat*
	Icteria virens *yellow-breasted chat*
	Mniotilta varia
	black and white warbler
	Parula americana *parula warbler*
	Protonotaria citrea
	prothonotary warbler
	Seiurus aurocapillus *ovenbird*
	S. noveboracensis
	northern waterthrush, others

Woolly Monkey

Woolly monkey

The woolly monkey is one of the commonest monkeys kept in captivity, yet very little is known about it in the wild. It is fairly large and is closely related to the spider monkey. Although only 16—22 in. long in head and body, with a tail of 22—28 in. long, it weighs 7½—20 lb, and is much fatter than the spider monkey. Like the spider monkey, however, it always seems to be pot-bellied. The woolly monkey has close, woolly fur and a black face which, in spite of the widely spaced nostrils, as in all New World monkeys, can look strikingly human, with a high and rounded forehead. The tail is prehensile, with a naked under-surface at the tip, covered with ridges and creases like fingerprints. This specialised skin is called volar skin.

Woolly monkeys live in the forests of South America. The common species is Humboldt's woolly monkey, which varies in colour in different areas from grey to pale brown or nearly black; often the head is black and the body pale. The very rare Hendee's woolly monkey, known from only a few specimens, is confined to a small area on the eastern flanks of the Andes. It is a deep mahogany colour with a yellow band underneath the end half of the tail, and a buff nose patch. It has never been seen alive by a European.

Mealtime acrobats

Humboldt's woolly monkey lives high in the trees, often in the emergent crowns which reach above the general forest canopy. In spite of its somewhat clumsy-looking build it is agile, and has the advantage of a 'fifth limb' in its tail, which is prehensile. With the help of this versatile appendage it can move among very thin branches, hanging underneath them, feeding with its hands while grasping with its tail only, or with its tail and one foot. It does not leap, but when it comes to an open space goes around it, or simply drops into a lower layer of branches. It does not seem to come to the ground at all in the wild. In captivity it generally flexes its hands on the ground, and walks in a somewhat ape-like manner. When resting, it sits upright, grasping with its tail. It sleeps curled up, with the tail wrapped around the body, or holding on to a branch.

Woolly monkeys have been seen in troops of 15—25, but they apparently do not hold territories. As in troops of spider monkeys, membership of a troop is probably not permanent. The troops of woolly monkeys often mix while feeding with troops of other monkeys, such as howlers or capuchins. The different species do not compete for food, but they do provide extra protection from predators, such as birds of prey or large snakes, because there are more eyes to keep a lookout for them.

Woolly monkeys feed on leaves and fruit. The signs of hard wear on their teeth seem to indicate that they eat a good deal of hard-shelled fruit.

Leonard Williams

△ *The agile acrobatics of woolly monkeys make them popular zoo animals. Their prehensile tail is in constant use as a 'fifth limb'.*

H Schifter

△ *Baby takes a ride as mother snacks non-chalantly. The young monkey stays aboard by gripping its parents short, thick fur.*

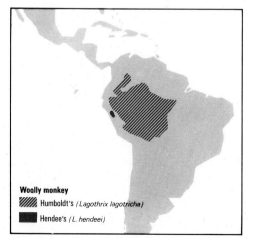

Woolly monkey

////// Humboldt's *(Lagothrix lagotricha)*

▮ Hendee's *(L. hendeei)*

Year-long infancy

As far as is known, there is no fixed breeding season although there may be a 'birth peak'. The gestation period is 7½ months, after which a single young is born. This is nursed for at least a year. Puberty is reached at four years, and the lifespan may be as much as 20 years.

Forgotten monkeys

Woolly monkeys are gentle and placid creatures, which makes them good pets. Some individuals, however, may become dangerous when they are older, but they are not as irritable as the Old World monkeys, and do not become bad-tempered with the same regularity. They have been submitted to intelligence tests, but not on a very wide scale. From what has been done they appear to be highly intelligent, like capuchins, and more so than an Old World monkey, although less so than an ape. They are so familiar in zoos and through Leonard Williams's books, that it is surprising that so little is known of their behaviour in the wild. All the more surprising is that so little is known of the 'forgotten' second species, Hendee's woolly monkey.

This was described as *Simia flavicauda* by Baron von Humboldt as long ago as 1812, at the same time as he described the more familiar species which is now named after him. Humboldt in fact saw only the trimmed, flat skins of the first species which were used as saddle covers by muleteers in Peru. Of the monkey itself he saw nothing, although its Peruvian name was given as *choro*. Pöppig mentioned reports of it in the same area near Yurimaguas, Maynas district, Peru, in 1832. Nothing more was heard of the species until Oldfield Thomas, of the British Museum (Natural History), obtained a skin from the same general area and described it as *Lagothrix hendeei*. He knew of Humboldt's description, but because of its somewhat sketchy nature and the worn nature of the skins Humboldt saw, Thomas considered it was not the same animal. The matter was not seriously considered again until 1963, when Jack Fooden pointed out that, in spite of the apparent discrepancies in the descriptions, the two forms must be the same animal, and that moreover it has an exceedingly restricted range in the San Martin and La Lejia areas of the Andes, about 5 000 feet above sea level. It is certainly the least known of all South American monkeys.

class	**Mammalia**
order	**Primates**
family	**Cebidae**
genus & species	***Lagothrix hendeei*** *Hendee's woolly monkey* ***L. lagotricha*** *Humboldt's woolly monkey*

▷ *The woolly monkey's furry skin was used as a saddle-cloth by the Peruvians 200 years ago.*

◁ *Overleaf: a wistful woolly monkey shows clearly the widely spaced and outward-facing nostrils of New World monkeys, or platyrrhines.*

Worm shell

Worm shells are a remarkable group of molluscs whose shells have come to resemble worm tubes. Because they are so odd nobody is quite sure what common name to give them — their various common names include tube molluscs, tube snails, worm shells and vermetids. They start life as quite ordinary little creeping snails with typical coiled shells, but soon they settle in one place and cement themselves to a rock or embed themselves in a sponge. Their shells, which may be various shades of cream, grey, pink or brown, then continue to grow either as long irregular tubes or in loose coils. Tube snails are limited to tropical and warm-temperate seas. They are now divided into two families, the Siliquariidae and the Vermetidae, which may possibly have evolved separately from more typical snails, since they differ in a number of important ways.

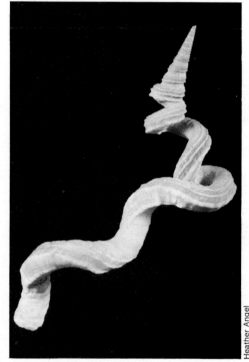

△ *The tortuous unravelled look of a worm shell.*
▷ *Fixed for life:* **Aletes squamigerus.**

Heather Angel

Feeding like barnacles

In the first family, the Siliquariidae, the shell becomes a loose spiral, like a corkscrew, embedded in the substratum. The first whorls form a narrow, tight spiral like the turret shells Turritellidae, from which the group may have evolved. The siliquariids feed by drawing water in over their single gills by the action of the cilia on them, a method also used by the sessile, but not closely related, slipper limpets. Diatoms and other particles become entangled in mucus and are propelled by cilia to the mouth. In *Siliquaria*, water leaves the body from a slit running the length of the shell. Another method of feeding has been observed in one member of the family, *Stephopoma*, which is unique among molluscs but reminiscent of the feeding of barnacles. The

gill filaments are extended out of the tube and, like the legs of barnacles, are swept through the water to trap small organisms.

Passive breeding

Since worm shells cannot move about, their eggs have to be fertilised by sperms carried in water currents into the mantle cavity of the female. The eggs of siliquariids are laid in separate capsules and are usually retained, lying free, in the mantle cavity, although in *Pyxipoma* there is a special brood pouch. The veliger stage is passed through in the egg and the young emerge as crawling snails and not as the free-swimming larvae we should expect as appropriate for the distribution of these otherwise sedentary animals. Like many other snails, the siliquariids have an operculum, that is, a horny

lid that can be pulled into place to close the aperture of the shell; this cover can be unusually elaborate and decorated with branched bristles. When the operculum is half closed, the bristles form a filter keeping out excessively large particles during feeding. The operculum can be put to another use by the embryo when ready to hatch. Its sharp edge may be used to cut through the wall of the egg capsule.

Slimy line-fishing

The members of the other family, the Vermetidae, have generally similar breeding habits except that several eggs are laid in one capsule and the capsules are attached inside the aperture of the mother's shell. The irregular tube-like shells of some of this family may be entwined together into

float in the water. After floating for a while, the threads are devoured as the many little grappling-hook teeth of the radula haul them into the mouth together with any captured prey or other particles.

Larger prey may be taken directly if it passes near the mouth. Strong feeding or respiratory currents would disturb the 'fishing lines' so it is understandable that the gills should be reduced. Likewise an operculum would be in the way, and this, also, is not present in the adult.

Evolution gone berserk

With these two species in mind, it is possible to speculate on their evolution from grazing ancestors, whose gills bore cilia just to create respiratory currents and sweep away sediment, to creeping snails using their gills for feeding, and so to fixed tube snails feeding in the same way and producing an excess of mucus that was eventually put to good use as a snare, while the gills reverted to their purely respiratory role. If this supposition is correct, then the production of mucus has gone almost to the point of

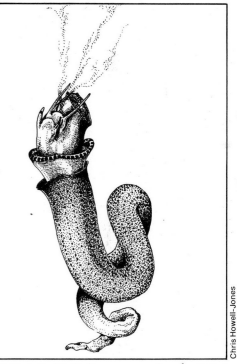

△ **Serpulorbis** *feeding: mucous strands up to a foot long trail on the surface, trapping food.*

s, sometimes forming large reefs or ;. Together with the tubeworms of the y Serpulidae and the stony corals or reporarians, they form the main con- ents of the miniature atolls or 'boilers' he Bermudas. The main points of in- st in this family centre around the erent methods of feeding. The evolu- ɪ of this habit is best illustrated by a nparison of two contrasting species. ·*pulorbis novaehollandiae* lives on the termost reefs of the Great Barrier Reef ɪd is one of the few snails to stand the ʰwerful battering of the waves. Its shell, hich can grow to a length of 10½ in., is ɪick and cemented all along its length o the dead coral rock. The mouth, some- imes 1½ in. across, can be closed by a horny operculum. It feeds by collecting particles from the incoming stream of water on the long, ciliated gill filaments. These particles become trapped in mucus which is propelled to the mouth. The bulk of the mucus is augmented by additional mucus balls from a gland below the mouth.

Serpulorbis gigas forms thinner-walled, twisted shells reaching about 8 in. in length and with an internal diameter up to ⅖ in. Most of the tube is not cemented to the rock but is raised up and often intertwined with others. *S. gigas* lives only in still water and feeds in a way that could not work in rough water but which is made easier by the raising of the shell aperture. The gland that in *S. novaehollandiae* merely supplements the mucus passing to the mouth is much better developed in *S. gigas* and produces long threads of slime, up to a foot long, that

madness in the scaled worm shell *S. squamigerus* of the American Pacific coast. In this species sheets of mucus up to 6 in. long are secreted, instead of strings, and those of neighbouring individuals tend to merge into one. So, when one worm shell starts to eat, all the others do so too.

phylum	**Mollusca**
class	**Gastropoda**
order	**Mesogastropoda**
families	**Siliquariidae**
	Vermetidae

DP Wilson

Wrasse

Wrasses are noted for their brilliant colours and for the way their colours and patterns vary with sex and age. Their belligerence, too, is exceptional.

A typical wrasse, and one whose behaviour is best known, is the cuckoo wrasse of the western Atlantic seaboard and the Mediterranean. It is long bodied, compressed laterally, with a long head and jaws. The lips are thick, the teeth in the front of the mouth well-developed and the angle of the jaw goes back nearly to the level of the large eye. The single dorsal fin is long, its front half spiny, the rear half soft-rayed. The anal fin is long, the tailfin square-ended, and the pelvics are forward on a level with the base of the pectorals. There are marked colour differences between the sexes. The male is yellow or orange with a vivid blue head and back with blue lines running over the gill-covers and along the flanks. Females and young fishes vary in colour from orange to red, with three spots on the rear half of the back.

The 600 species range from 3in. slender fishes to 10ft giants which weigh several hundred pounds, and are most numerous in tropical seas. Some of the small wrasses are cleaner fishes (p 140). One of the most colourful of the larger wrasses is the Atlantic bluehead. The males are blue with black bands in the front half and green in the rear half including the crescentic tail. The females and immatures range from yellow to green. Other Atlantic species are the corkwing or sea pheasant, rainbow wrasse and the ballan wrasse, on the European side, and the pudding wife, tautog, razorfish and hogfish on the American side.

Home-loving fishes

Wrasses are solitary fishes that live, at the most in pairs or trios, seldom in schools, in shallow seas, around rocky coasts and coral reefs. Some species live between tidemarks and shelter in rock pools when the tide is out. Another marked feature of their behaviour is the tendency for each fish to keep to one place from which it makes feeding sorties. This is most marked in the species that have become cleaner fishes, but with other wrasses, also, observers have commented how they could rely on seeing the same fish in the same place. They are rock-haunters which swim by twisting movements of the rear part of the dorsal fin and the anal fin helped by backward beats of the pectorals. When speed is needed this is supplemented by movements of the whole body, but the fin swimming allows them to manoeuvre nimbly in confined spaces, as in rock crevices.

The strict territorial behaviour of wrasses is linked with their habitual aggressiveness. Their attacks take the form of biting off each other's fins or gouging out the eyes, and the extent and effectiveness of them can be judged from the reduction of numbers in one large tank, which originally contained 70 Hawaiian saddle wrasses; only a dozen remained after three months.

Armed with fangs

The strong and prominent front teeth which create such havoc include the one or more fang-like teeth in the side of each jaw. They are normally used to feed on crabs and sea snails as well as smaller fishes. Wrasses eat probably any animal food, including carrion, since they are often caught in crab and lobster pots which they seem to have entered to feed on the bait.

Rough courtship

Some wrasses construct their nests of seaweed and corallines wedged in a rock crevice, both sexes helping in the work. The eggs are laid in the middle of this tangled mass but there is no evidence that the parents guard the eggs. In others a shallow trough is dug in the sand in which the eggs are laid. Spawning seems to be preceded by a courtship, judging from the observations set forth by Douglas P Wilson in 1956. During one night in May, in the Plymouth Laboratory aquarium, Wilson watched a male cuckoo wrasse dig a nest in the sand by turning on his side and flapping vigorously with his tail. After that he attacked all the females around him, charging at them and nibbling them until he at last induced one to follow him to the nest. During this excited behaviour the male went white over a large area of the head and back, which may have acted as a visual stimulus to the female. The eggs, $\frac{1}{25}$ in. in diameter, hatch in 21 days, the baby fishes becoming planktonic. Cuckoo wrasse are believed to live up to 17 years.

Problems of colour

The bright colours of wrasses have more than artistic merit—they pose problems worthy of further thought. To start with wrasses are one of the few groups of fishes in which females and males differ markedly in colour. The next point is that while it is not unusual for fishes living around gaudily coloured coral reefs to be brightly coloured, presumably being camouflaged against their background, it is unusual for their relatives in temperate seas to be equally brightly coloured. Presumably wrasses have few enemies, so can be brightly coloured with impunity. This idea is supported by those wrasses that act as cleaners, a trade they could not carry out without an unusual immunity from attack. There are even species, of blennies for example, that mimic their shape and colours, a sure sign that these are protective. By contrast, there are a number of wrasses in the South Pacific that look like lumps of floating weed. They are a translucent green with dark brown lines and white blotches. Moreover, they hold themselves limp so they are carried back and forth in the surf, as seaweed would be: an effective camouflage.

G Mundey

Fishes abed

Those who say we can rely on seeing the same wrasse in the same place each day are supported by the findings of those who have studied wrasses in marine aquaria. These find that wrasses spend much time resting on rock ledges or in crevices during the day, and that the fishes go to these same places at night to sleep—and they lie on their sides to do so. More remarkable are the findings of WA Gosline and V Brock that the wrasses around Hawaii bury themselves in the sand at night to sleep. When these wrasses are kept in an aquarium they swim about all day and at night the aquaria look empty. All the fishes seem to disappear. Of the 48 species studied only one does not go into the sand to sleep. This is *Labroides phthirophagus*, which surrounds itself with a mucous envelope, a sort of nightdress, like the parrotfish, mentioned on page 1708.

class	**Pisces**
order	**Perciformes**
family	**Labridae**
genera & species	***Coris julis*** *rainbow wrasse*
	Crenilabrus melops *corkwing*
	Halichoeres radiatus
	pudding wife
	Labrus bergylta *ballan wrasse*
	*L. **mixtus** cuckoo wrasse*
	Lachnolaimus maximus *hogfish*
	Tautoga onitis *tautog*
	Thalassoma bifasciatum
	Atlantic bluehead
	Xyriclithys psittacus *razorfish*
	others

ES Hobson

△ *Purples and greens:* **Thalassoma ruppelli** *exhibits a wide range of subtle hues.*
◁△ *Blues and yellows: male cuckoo wrasse in breeding colour — a northern species which ranges from Norway to the Mediterranean.*
◁ *Spawning aggregation of* **Thalassoma lucasanum** *in the Gulf of California.*

A cosy nest in a damp situation: a European wren feeds its young with a tasty morsel.

Wren

In Europe the wren is a widespread and well-known bird of woodland and gardens. In Britain it is known affectionately as the Jenny wren; but it is the only European representative of a family that is otherwise confined to the New World. In Australia and New Zealand there is a large group of birds known as wrens or warblers which includes, among others, the thornbills, emu-wrens and blue-wrens. In New Zealand, a third group of 'wrens' consists of the bush wren, rock wren and rifleman.

The true wrens of the family Troglodytidae are mainly small, drab-coloured birds, but the cactus wren of the south-western United States and Mexico is 8 in. long. There are about 60 species, the most widespread being the wren of Europe, Asia and North Africa, which is also found in North America where it is known as the winter wren. It is 3¾ in. long and although it is popularly thought to be the smallest British bird, this honour is held by the goldcrest (p 910). In appearance it has the typical characters of other wrens: dumpy body, short, upturned tail, rounded wings, slender bill and brown plumage, lighter underneath with black bars on wings and tail.

A very widespread American wren is the house wren which ranges from southern Canada to Cape Horn and is one of three wrens found on the Falkland Islands. It is very similar in appearance to the winter wren. Bewick's wren has a white eyestripe and white underparts, and the cactus wren has a white breast densely spotted with black. The zapata wren was discovered only in 1926 and is restricted to a single swamp on the coast of Cuba.

Preference for undergrowth

The typical habitat of wrens is low, fairly dense undergrowth but the cactus wren and the rock wren—not to be confused with the New Zealand rock wren—are found in rocky desert country with sparse vegetation, the short-billed marsh wren and the zapata wren live in marshes, and several tropical wrens live on the floor of rain forests. Few wrens, except those living in the far north, migrate. The European wren suffers in hard winters when the ground below the undergrowth is covered by snow and after the severe winter of 1963 when their numbers in Britain were severely reduced, it was possible to determine their preference for different habitats. By means of a painstaking survey over several years it was shown that the surviving wrens set up territories in woodland and in well-covered banks of streams. As their numbers recovered they spread first into orchards and gardens and then into hedges.

Varied, delightful songs

As they usually live among undergrowth wrens are more often heard than seen. They have a variety of calls and rich songs which are surprisingly loud for such small birds. Some tropical wrens sing antiphonally, the pair keeping in contact in dense cover by singing in turn. The song of the winter wren is a shrill warble ending with a trill. It can be heard all the year round and is used for a variety of purposes apart from advertising the territory. EA Armstrong has, in his monograph *The Wren*, classified the variety of the wren's song. The loudest songs are territorial, defying males and attracting females, then there is a harsher song heard when a wren is challenging another bird. Softer, quieter songs are used in courtship and for inviting the female to inspect a nest while the softest song is heard from females as they sit on the nest. A fairly loud song is also heard when wrens are gathering at a communal roost.

A fishing wren

Wrens feed mainly on insects, particularly caterpillars, fly larvae, beetles, bugs and so on, which they find in crevices and on foliage. Cactus wrens turn over stones in their search for insects and European wrens have been known to catch small fish.

A wife in each nest

Most wrens build domed nests but some, such as the house wrens which often use nest-boxes, build cup-shaped nests in holes and crevices. In monogamous species both sexes build the nest but in polygamous species such as the European wrens and the marsh wrens the male builds the nest and the female lines it. These wrens may build several nests in their territories, some of which are ignored, or are used only for roosting.

Polygamy is related to an abundant food supply but in all cases the female alone incubates the eggs, although she may be fed by the male. The clutch ranges from 2 or 3 in the tropics to 8–10 in temperate regions and incubation takes about two weeks. The chicks fly in another two weeks and the male helps feed them. There is more than one brood in a year and in the house wren the young of one brood may help feed the young of the next.

Wrens in dormitories

Wrens frequently roost under cover, working their way into crevices, holes in trees, old nests, even into pockets of clothes hanging out to dry, and some tropical wrens build special roosting nests. Wrens are usually solitary but they may gather to roost communally; 61 European wrens were once counted roosting in a nest box. Communal roosting occurs most frequently in hard weather and it appears that wrens remember suitable roosting sites for future use. As dusk gathers the wrens gather and it seems that they follow a leader who calls or sings to them in a particular way. As more wrens fly in to join the group they chase from perch to perch until they finally enter their roost arranging themselves tier upon tier with heads directed inwards.

class	**Aves**
order	**Passeriformes**
family	**Troglodytidae**
genera & species	***Campylorhynchus bruneicapillus*** *cactus wren*
	Cistophorus platensis *short-billed marsh wren*
	Ferminia cerverai *zapata wren*
	Salpinctes obsoletus *rock wren*
	Thryomanes bewickii *Bewick's wren*
	Troglodytes aedon *house wren*
	T. troglodytes *winter or European wren*